SCHOLASTIC

NO FUSS

YEAR 4
PHOTOCOPIABLES

All you need to teach 11 curriculum subjects!

AGES 8-9

- Levelled and linked to the curriculum

- Stand-alone photocopiable activities

- Ideal for mixed-age classes

Paul Noble and Jean Noble

AUTHORS
Paul Noble and Jean Noble

DEVELOPMENT EDITOR
Kate Pedlar

PROJECT EDITOR
Fabia Lewis

DESIGNERS
Q2a Media

COVER DESIGN
Anna Oliwa

ILLUSTRATOR
Sarah Warburton

ACKNOWLEDGEMENTS
Oxford University Press for the use of 'I've been to Harlem', from *Sing Together* (Oxford University Press). Stainer & Bell Ltd for the use of 'A Christmas Carol', by Sydney Carter © Stainer & Bell Ltd (Galliard). Ordnance Survey for the use of extracts of maps licensed from Ordnance Survey® with the permission of the Controller of Her Majesty's Stationery Office © 2008, Crown copyright. All rights reserved. Ordnance Survey Licence No. 100039768.

Text © 2008, Paul Noble and Jean Noble
© 2008, Scholastic Ltd

Published by Scholastic Ltd
Villiers House
Clarendon Avenue
Leamington Spa
Warwickshire
CV32 5PR
www.scholastic.co.uk
Designed using Adobe InDesign
Printed by Bell & Bain Ltd, Glasgow

1 2 3 4 5 6 7 8 9   8 9 0 1 2 3 4 5 6 7

British Library Cataloguing-in-Publication Data
A catalogue record for this book is available from the British Library.

ISBN 978-1407-10096-8

The rights of Paul Noble and Jean Noble to be identified as the authors of this work have been asserted by them in accordance with the Copyright, Designs and Patents Act 1988.

Crown copyright material reproduced under the terms of the Click Use Licence © Crown copyright.

Photocopiable pages first published in *Year Group Photocopiables Year 4* (first published 2003).

www.scholastic.co.uk

CONTENTS

CONTENTS

SCHOLASTIC
www.scholastic.co.uk

INTRODUCTION

This is a straightforward compilation of stand-alone photocopiable activities for children in Year 4. Instead of including lengthy teachers' notes, alongside these activity sheets we have devised a concise and factual **curriculum grid**, which, in note form, cross-references the content of the sheets to the National Curriculum, the Primary Framework and where appropriate, to the Curriculum for Excellence (Scotland). Objectives for each activity sheet are stated and brief notes are given for guidance on use.

Within the curriculum grid, links are also made to National Curriculum Attainment Targets and attainment levels and to the non-statutory Attainment Targets in RE as well as to the non-statutory guidelines at Key Stage 2 for PSHE and Citizenship. Before you use any sheet it is recommended that you refer to the curriculum grid so that you are clear about the sheet's objectives and are aware of any special demands made by the activity.

The 'photocopiable worksheet' has not always had a good press – there are copying issues to contend with as well as the occasional question mark over quality. Yet arguably, in spite of the high-tech gizmos now available, they are still the most useful teaching aid invented since a stick of chalk first squeaked its way across a chalkboard. However, when a worksheet is handed out, you cannot assume that intellectual activity is immediately stimulated in children. It still remains for you to capture children's interest and to provide the intellectual stimulus and practical experience that may be required to make the worksheet work.

In Year 4, children face the whole range of curriculum subjects as before, as well as the phased repetition of some basic concepts, processes and skills introduced at an earlier stage. But there is also new subject matter to be tackled in every aspect of the curriculum so there is no reason why progress should splutter to a halt to make Year 4 a 'drifter's year'. Learning is as new and exciting as ever.

The National Curriculum, prescriptive though it may be, still involves making choices and because we cannot cover everything in a book such as this, we have relied heavily upon the schemes of work drawn up by the Qualifications and Curriculum Authority to help us make our choices. These schemes are acknowledged as the basis for many school syllabuses so, with QCA guidelines to hand, we have tried to stick to the most obvious routes.

You should find this book particularly helpful when you are limited by time or have to meet the needs of voracious learners. Supply teachers and others 'caught on the hop' will also be able to rely on this material to help them to cope with demanding days.

Page	Activity	Objectives	Teachers' notes	NC, QCA & Primary Framework	Curriculum for Excellence (Scotland)	AT links and levels
15	Words containing 'k'	To recognise common letter strings and critical features of words.	Decent dictionaries will be an asset. Highlight and extend other patterns in the words, that is, 'kn', 'ck' and 'sk'.	Literacy Strand 6 – Word structure and spelling	LIT 010N/X – Tools for reading LIT 120X – Tools for writing	AT2 Level 2 AT3 Level 2
16	Words ending in 'y'	To examine what happens to words ending in 'y' when changes are made and to notice patterns in the changes.	This sheet should be used as part of teaching about word patterns and spelling strategies. Where there is a vowel before the final 'y' the new word is made by adding 's'; where there is not, the 'y' is replaced by 'i' and then 'es' is added.	Literacy Strand 6 – Word structure and spelling	LIT 010N/X – Tools for reading LIT 120X – Tools for writing	AT2 Level 2
17	One of our consonants is missing!	To identify misspelled words. To spell words containing double consonants.	Focus on the correct. Get children to obliterate the wrong spelling. The middle consonant is doubled in each case.	Literacy Strand 6 – Word structure and spelling	LIT 010N/X – Tools for reading LIT 120X – Tools for writing	AT2 Level 2 AT3 Level 3
18	Adding 'ing' to verbs	To spell verbs that end in 'ing'.	The children link the words using a pencil line. The explanation on the sheet about colour coding will probably need reiterating.	Literacy Strand 6 – Word structure and spelling	LIT 010N/X – Tools for reading LIT 120X – Tools for writing	AT2 Level 2 AT3 Level 3
19	Tagged on the end: suffixes	To recognise and spell the suffixes -hood, -al, -ary, -ship, and -ness.	The exercise is not difficult but children may need support to read some of the root words. Encourage the use of dictionaries to find meanings.	Literacy Strand 6 – Word structure and spelling	LIT 010N/X – Tools for reading LIT 120X – Tools for writing	AT2 Level 2 AT3 Level 3
20	Finding adverbs	To find and list alternative adverbs for sentences.	This is an open-ended activity that allows for a range of answers. You should give credit for the most appropriate and powerful words. Draw attention to the fact that many adverbs end in 'ly'.	Literacy Strand 6 – Word structure and spelling; Strand 11 – Sentence structure and punctuation	LIT 010N/X – Tools for reading LIT 120X – Tools for writing	AT2 Level 2 AT3 Level 3
21	Homophones	To be able to distinguish spellings and meanings of common homophones.	Stress that all that homophones have in common is how they sound; meanings and spellings are different. The words in brackets at the end of the sentences are used to supply the missing word for both of the preceding sentence's gaps.	Literacy Strand 6 – Word structure and spelling	LIT 010N/X – Tools for reading LIT 120X – Tools for writing	AT2 Level 2 AT3 Level 3
22	The tense connection	To understand that the tense of a verb can be changed.	That 'tense' refers to time needs to be taught. Discuss the answers when the sheet has been completed.	Literacy Strand 6 – Word structure and spelling	LIT 010N/X – Tools for reading	AT2 Level 2/3
23	Belongs to…	To use an apostrophe (for possession) correctly.	There is rather a lot on this sheet so don't use it 'cold'. You could use one section of the sheet at a time.	Literacy Strand 11 – Sentence structure and punctuation	LIT 010N/X – Tools for reading LIT 120X; LIT 121Y – Tools for writing	AT2 Level 3 AT3 Level 3
24	Its or it's?	To know the difference between contraction and possession in the use of an apostrophe. To use its and it's correctly.	You will need to go over the principle involved here more than once before letting children loose on this sheet. Teach the simple 'it is' replacement test and they should be able to complete the exercise without errors.	Literacy Strand 11 – Sentence structure and punctuation	LIT 010N/X – Tools for reading LIT 120X; LIT 121Y – Tools for writing	AT2 Level 3 AT3 Level 3/4
25	Punctuation marks	To identify punctuation marks in text. To read with awareness of punctuation.	It is a good idea to let the children work in pairs on this activity. The first part is simply a question of knowledge. They may find dictionaries useful.	Literacy Strand 11 – Sentence structure and punctuation	LIT 010N/X – Tools for reading LIT 120X; LIT 121Y – Tools for writing	AT2 Level 2/3 AT3 Level 3/4
26	Compound words	To spell compound words. To know that the identification of compound words can help spelling where pronunciation is not helpful (as in 'cupboard').	The pictures are clues not answers. (The first one is 'cupboard' not 'mugbox'.) Answers are: 1. cupboard 2. handbag 3. football 4. toothbrush 5. honeymoon 6. gooseberry 7. buttercup 8. bulldog 9. drumstick 10. rainbow 11. nutcracker 12. pushchair 13. matchbox 14. sunflower 15. grapefruit 16. ladybird.	Literacy Strand 6 – Word structure and spelling	LIT 010N/X – Tools for reading LIT 120X – Tools for writing	AT3 Level 3
27	Poem parts	To recognise and understand terms that identify specific parts of a poem.	Read the poem for enjoyment first, perhaps on a separate occasion to the one when the sheet is to be completed. Decent dictionaries are needed. Mark the text as a class exercise with lots of accompanying explanation; the sheet may become a messy.	Literacy Strand 10 – Text structure and organisation	LIT 114Q – Finding and using information (reading) ENG 101 A/L/W – Enjoyment and choice (reading)	AT2 Level 2/3
28	Points of view	To write a persuasive letter that presents a specific point of view. To organise and link arguments together effectively in writing.	Have a session where the class evaluates arguments from the sheet. Which is the most important argument? Which points might be discarded? Which point should be made first?	Literacy Strand 7 – Understanding and interpreting texts; Strand 9 – Creating and shaping texts	LIT 2222 – Tools for writing LIT 124AB – Organising and using information LIT 228 AF – Creating texts	AT3 Level 3

NO FUSS
PHOTOCOPIABLE

Page	Activity	Objectives	Teachers' notes	NC, QCA & Primary Framework	Curriculum for Excellence (Scotland)	AT links and levels
29	Purr-suasion	To evaluate advertisements. To recognise some of the devices and strategies used when advertising a product.	You might make an OHT and use it for class discussion. The advertisement uses: humour, exaggerated claims, memorable jingles, special offers, attention grabbing strategies and evidence.	Literacy Strand 7 – Understanding and interpreting texts; Strand 8 – Engaging with and responding to texts	LIT 218U – Understanding, analysing and evaluating (reading)	AT2 Level 3
30	Making a new ending	To be able to write an alternative ending to a familiar story.	Children use the writing frame on the sheet to help them. Focus solely on the ending so that the task need not involve the writing of a lengthy script.	Literacy Strand 9 – Creating and shaping texts	LIT 121Y – Tools for writing	AT3 Level 2/3
31	Writing up notes	To write a report through extending brief notes into connected prose.	Make sure that this is not just a cut-and-paste exercise. Encourage the use of clear, connected and coherent prose.	Literacy Strand 9 – Creating and shaping texts	LIT 224AB – Organising and using information (writing)	AT3 Level 3
32	Edit this	To edit a story by deleting the less important or repetitive elements.	Read the story to the class first. Explain what is required for the editing. *What unimportant bits could be left out?*	Literacy Strand 10 – Text structure and organisation	LIT 125AC – Organising and using information (writing)	AT3 Level 3
33	A simile poem	To understand the use of similes. To begin to use similes in writing.	Explain what a simile is first. If the children use the picture clues the first part of the exercise should be straightforward. The first set of similes describes the man's exit from the room and the second set, an old man's character and appearance.	Literacy Strand 9 – Creating and shaping texts; Strand 11 – Sentence structure and organisation	ENG 128AH – Creating texts	AT3 Level 3
34	Groups of adjectives	To collect and make lists of adjectives that have similar meanings.	Note that the sheet requires the use of a thesaurus.	Literacy Strand 6 – Word structure and spelling	LIT 113P – Tools for reading	AT2 Level 2
35	Placing adverbs	To identify and use adverbs correctly in sentences.	This helps to establish in children's minds that not all adverbs end in 'ly'.	Literacy Strand 11 – Sentence structure and organisation	LIT 221Y – Tools for writing	AT2 Level 2/3
36	What would you have done?	To write about situations that arise in stories linking to personal experience.	The writing frame is intended to help children formulate coherent responses based upon their own feelings and experiences: they have to put themselves 'in the frame' as it were.	Literacy Strand 9 – Creating and shaping texts	LIT 125AC – Organising and using information ENG 229AG – Creating texts	AT3 Level 3
37	Words and numbers	To know what each of the digits in a number represents including 0 as a place holder. To be able to partition four-digit numbers.	Check understanding of the term 'digit'. Answers are: **1.** The biggest number is 65,431 and the smallest 13,456 **2.** The biggest number is 54,320 and the smallest is either 20,345 or 2345. (If the latter answer is given ask the child to explain that 0 is used as a place holder in the ten thousand column) **3.** 6,000, 700, 30, 1 and 7,000.	Maths Strand – Counting and understanding number	MNU 102B – Number processes	AT2 Level 3
38	Approximate	To be able to round numbers to the nearest 10 or 100. To identify the best approximations for calculations.	A sound understanding of the number system is essential before pencil and paper calculations or calculators can be expected to yield sensible answers. Round up when the numbers are halfway. Answers are: 40kg; 440m; 40 miles; 250; 2360 miles; 30 minutes; 500; 500; 1600; 100; 900; 9400; 20 × 5; 700 + 200; 50 × 20.	Maths Strand – Knowing and using number facts	MNU 101A – Estimation and rounding	AT2 Level 3
39	Negative integers	To recognise and place negative and positive integers on a number line in order.	Teach the term 'integer' (negative numbers are integers too). Children need to know that number lines can cross and extend beyond zero. Incorrect answers will be readily apparent.	Maths Strands – Counting and understanding number; Calculating	MNU 206 – Negative numbers	AT2 Level 3
40	Equivalent fractions (1)	To use the notation of fractions. To use diagrams to identify equivalence between fractions.	Work with the class first. Count the segments and name the fractions. Answers are: $\frac{2}{8}$; $\frac{2}{6}$; $\frac{4}{6}$; $\frac{2}{10}$; $\frac{6}{8}$; $\frac{1}{2}$; $\frac{4}{10}$. Children may learn these equivalent fractions by rote.	Maths Strand – Counting and understanding number	MTH 106H – Fractions, decimals and percentages	AT2 Level 3
41	Equivalent fractions (2)	To use the notation of fractions. To identify equivalence between fractions.	This is an extension of the last sheet. Answers are: $\frac{1}{4}$; $\frac{2}{4}$; $\frac{6}{8}$; $\frac{1}{3}$. The remainder must be marked visually.	Maths Strand – Counting and understanding number	MTH 106H – Fractions, decimals and percentages	AT2 Level 3
42	Decimal places	To order decimal numbers on number line. To use decimal notation when converting pence to pounds and centimetres to metres.	Do not use this sheet 'cold'. Decimals are best introduced by using a model that the children know, for example the currency system. Answers are: £4.52; £2.22; £17.36; £5.25; £6.94; £9.62; 2.36m; 4.86m; 1.32m; 0.26m; 92.32m; 4.11m.	Maths Strand – Counting and understanding number	MNU 104H; MNU 208H – Fractions, decimals and percentages	AT2 Level 3

Page	Activity	Objectives	Teachers' notes	NC, QCA & Primary Framework	Curriculum for Excellence (Scotland)	AT links and levels
43	Check it out!	To check calculations using the inverse operation.	Explain the examples at the top of the sheet. It is easiest to check visually whether children are using the correct method – method being more important than answers here. Answers are: correct; correct; correct; incorrect; correct; incorrect; correct; incorrect; correct, correct.	Maths Strands – Knowing and using number facts; Calculating	MNU 103C – Addition, subtraction, multiplication and division	AT2 Level 2/3
44	Number problems	To choose and use operations of +, –, × and + appropriately to solve word problems involving numbers in real life.	Words that usually clarify sometimes confuse children when mixed with numbers. Encourage a systematic and logical approach and the writing down of the number element of the problems. Words are needed in the answers. Answers are: 104 legs; the following Monday; 13 spoonfuls; 24 children; 17.	Maths Strands – Using and applying mathematics; Calculating	MNU 203C – Addition, subtraction, multiplication and division	AT1 Level 2/3 AT2 Level 2/3
45	Put it another way	To use language related to measures. To be able to recognise how familiar units are linked.	Children might learn and remember the boxed facts before attempting the sheet proper. Answers are: 1. 1.5kg 322g 2. 2kg 129g 3. 9kg 3g 4. 10kg 42g 5. 2m 26cm 6. 5m 72cm 7. 14m 35cm 8. 9m 4cm 9. 2l 467ml 10. 1l 324ml 11. 5l 100ml 12. 6l 8ml.	Maths Strands – Counting and understanding number; Measuring	MNU 218M – Measurement	AT3 Level 3
46	Measuring scales	To read a scale with a suitable degree of accuracy.	This sheet is self-explanatory. Answers: 1. 450ml 2. 1.5kg 3. 47 seconds 4. 120ml 5. 55cm.	Maths Strand – Measuring	MNU 218M – Measurement	AT3 Level 2/3
47	Journey round the edge: perimeter	To be able to measure and calculate the perimeters of simple shapes.	Children must be able to measure accurately. Make sure the rulers used are in good order before the start. Addition can be avoided by 'measuring on' from the finishing point each time. Some children may prefer to use mental strategies to calculate answers. Answers are: 1. 15cm 2. 24cm 3. 20cm 4. 28cm 5. 12cm.	Maths Strands – Calculating; Measuring	MNU 219M – Measurement	AT3 Level 4
48	Tangram	To find the area of a shape by counting squares on a grid. To begin to understand that the area of a shape is unchanged no matter how the space it occupies is arranged.	A fun exercise that demonstrates the conservation of area. Let children play with the shapes to create what they will. The area of the tangram is 256cm². The method used to arrive at this figure will depend upon the ability of the children.	Maths Strand – Measuring	MNU 219M – Measurement	AT3 Level 4
49	Make a date	To know and use the language related to dates and time.	A useful addition to this sheet would be a current calendar.	Maths Strand – Measuring	MNU 110L – Time	AT2 Level 2
50	Time for TV	To be able to solve problems related to time and to read information from timetables.	Show children the printed TV schedule and quiz them on its use. Answers are: 1. 1 hour 2. 1 hour 20 minutes 3. Relatives 4. 3:22 5. 4 hours assuming the News and Weather is watched at 6.00 for ten minutes, but you should accept 3 hours 50 minutes, which excludes the latter. Ask children to explain their answers.	Maths Strands – Using and applying mathematics; Calculating; Measuring	MNU 111L; MNU 214L – Time	AT1 level 2 AT3 Level 3
51	Put Polly in a polygon	To be able to name and label polygons correctly.	For the exercise to be worthwhile the children must name the polygon as well as draw Polly. Not all the shape names have been given. Provide an additional wordbank as required.	Maths Strand – Understanding shape	MTH 119S – Properties of 2D shapes and 3D objects	AT3 Level 2
52	Building with cubes	To start to visualise 3D shapes from 2D drawings.	In the first instance children should try to follow the instructions without using apparatus. Answers are: 16; 8; 12; 14.	Maths Strand – Understanding shape	MTH 120S – Properties of 2D shapes and 3D objects	AT3 Level 3/4
53	Ordered pairs	To describe points on a grid using pairs of numbers (coordinates).	To prepare you may first like to play a version of noughts and crosses with the class, using a numbered grid. (Remember to use the numbered lines not the squares.) The answers can be written on the sheet alongside the letters on the grid. Answers are: A (1,2) B (1,7) C (2,6) D (3,3) E (4,8) F (4,5) G (5,4) H (6,7) I (7,1) J (8,9) K (8,6) L (8,1).	Maths Strand – Understanding shape	MTH 230U – Angles, symmetry and transformation	AT3 Level 2/3
54	Horizontal and vertical	To be able to recognise and identify examples of horizontal and vertical objects.	The sheet should be marked by reference to the pictures.	Maths Strand – Understanding shape	MTH 226T – Angles, symmetry and transformation	AT3 Level 2/3

NO FUSS
PHOTOCOPIABLE

SCHOLASTIC
www.scholastic.co.uk

Page	Activity	Objectives	Teachers' notes	NC, QCA & Primary Framework	Curriculum for Excellence (Scotland)	AT links and levels
55	Sizing up angles	To place a set of angles in order of size.	Precise measurement in degrees should not be required. All angles are less than 180. Answers: **1.** A, D, C, **2.** B, D, C, A **3.** A, B, D, C **4.** D, C, B, A.	Maths Strand – Understanding shape	MTH 226T – Angles, symmetry and transformation	AT3 Level 2/3
56	A question of degrees	To make and describe turns using compass directions.	Demonstrate angles as rotation using clock hands, children etc. Answers are: 90° clockwise; 45° anti-clockwise; 90° anti-clockwise; 45° clockwise. For the second question: 90°; 180°; 270°; 360°; 135°; 315°. (Start at North each time.)	Maths Strand – Understanding shape	MTH 226T; MTH 228T – Angles, symmetry and transformation	AT3 Level 2/3
57	Sort by sets	To use a Venn diagram to sort and display information about numbers.	This is simply sorting by numerical attribute. It does involve placing some numbers in both sets simultaneously – check the children understand what should happen.	Maths Strands – Knowing and using number facts; Handling data	MTH 207E – Multiples, factors and primes MNU 125W – Data and analysis	AT2 Level 2/3 AT4 Level 2/3
58	Get sorted!	To sort and display information about numbers and shapes using a Carroll diagram.	Demonstrate how a Carroll diagram works by sorting quantities in the way shown on the sheet.	Maths Strands – Knowing and using number facts; Handling data	MTH 207E – Multiples, factors and primes MNU 125W – Data and analysis	AT2 Level 3 AT3 Level 3 AT4 Level 2/3
59	The human skeleton	To know that humans have bony skeletons inside their bodies. To understand that their skeleton grows as they grow. To locate major bones in the human body.	Visual aids are a great asset when doing this work. Full calcification of the human skeleton takes about 20 years at which point it contains about 5kg of mineral salts. The 'stirrup' bone in the ear is the smallest bone and the 'femur' (thigh) is the largest.	Science NC: Sc2 Humans and other animals QCA: Unit 4A Moving and growing	SCN 009M – Keeping my body healthy	AT2 Level 3
60	Vertebrates	To examine, make predictions about and compare features of different bony skeletons.	The text draws attention to the connection between the skeletal structure and the nature of the animal. Answers: **1.** hare **2.** cat. A copy of the preceding sheet will help with the final question.	Science NC: Sc2 Humans and other animals QCA: Unit 4A Moving and growing	SCN 205B – Biodiversity	AT2 Level 3
61	Animals without bony skeletons	To understand that all bodies need support but that not all animals have internal skeletons to do this.	Teach the word 'invertebrate'. Answers: snail (supported on the outside of the body); worm (by its skin); crab (shell on the outside); locust (external shell).	Science NC: Sc2 Life processes; Humans and other animals QCA: Unit 4A Moving and growing	SCN 205B – Biodiversity	AT2 Level 3
62	Muscles and movement	To learn that animals with skeletons have muscles attached to their bones and that a muscle has to contract (shorten) to make a bone move.	Teach the information as on the sheet. Test out the equipment first – the springs must not be too strong for safety reasons. Muscles cannot push and they only generate movement when they shorten, which is why they work in pairs.	Science NC: Sc2 Humans and other animals QCA: Unit 4A Moving and growing	SCN 111M – Keeping my body healthy	AT2 Level 3/4
63	Organisms	To learn that the term 'organism' means living thing. To sort organisms into plants and animals.	'Organism' is a general term for all living things. Note that 'fungi' are now placed in a separate category from plants.	Science NC: Sc2 Life processes QCA: Unit 4B Habitats	SCN 102B – Biodiversity	AT2 Level 2/3
64	Habitats	To identify types of habitats. To recognise that different animals are found in different habitats.	A straightforward sheet.	Science NC: Sc2 Life processes QCA: Unit 4B Habitats	SCN 205B – Biodiversity	AT2 Level 2/3
65	Identification keys	To group organisms according to observed features. To use branching keys to identify particular plants and animals.	Talk through the exercise first. Children will need paper to work with. Answers are: **1.** bee **2.** centipede **3.** spider. (Note that a harvestman is commonly known as a 'daddy-long-legs'.)	Science NC: Sc1 Investigative skills; Sc2 Life processes; Variation and classification QCA: Unit 4B Habitats	SCN 102B; SCN 205B – Biodiversity	AT1 Level 2/3 AT2 Level 2
66	Food chains	To understand what a food chain is and that most food chains start with a green plant.	Teach the terms 'producer' and 'food chain'. Answers are: leaves – worms – birds – cats. The producer is 'leaves'.	Science NC: Sc2 Life processes; Feeding relationships QCA: Unit 4B Habitats	SCN 205B – Biodiversity SCN 214F – Energy transfer	AT2 Level 3/4
67	Thermo-meters	To understand that a thermometer measures how hot or cold things are (temperature).	Research will be required so ensure that books and materials are to hand. Answers are: a clinical thermometer; a forehead thermometer; a maximum and minimum thermometer (one that measures two temperatures over a set period); a thermostik (soil/dipping thermometer). Examples should be demonstrated.	Science NC: Sc1 Investigative skills QCA: Unit 4C Keeping warm	SCN 104D – Climate and Earth science	AT1 Level 3

Page	Activity	Objectives	Teachers' notes	NC, QCA & Primary Framework	Curriculum for Excellence (Scotland)	AT links and levels
68	Wrap up!	To suggest ways to test how cold things can be kept cold.	Materials and equipment will be required. Children need to explain how they would set up a fair test. Before testing, make sure that the test is safe and sensible.	Science NC: Sc1 Scientific enquiry; Investigative skills; Sc3 Grouping and classifying materials QCA: Unit 4C Keeping warm	SCN 115X – Properties and uses	AT1 Level 3 AT3 Level 3
69	Keeping solids and liquids apart	To correctly classify materials as liquid or solid.	Identify the contents, not the containers. Note a sponge is a solid that can change shape due to the air within it. Solid, liquid and gas are states of matter into which all substances on Earth can exist, given the right circumstances. (Rock is liquid in a volcano.)	Science NC: Sc3 Grouping and classifying materials QCA: Unit 4D Solids, liquids and how they can be separated	SCI 115X – Properties and uses	AT1 Level 3 AT3 Level 3
70	Separate (1)	To understand that solids can be mixed and that it is often possible to get the original materials back through separation.	Equipment is needed for this experiment sheet. Answers will vary depending on the mix and the method of separation.	Science NC: Sc3 Separating mixtures of materials QCA: Unit 4D Solids, liquids and how they can be separated	SCN 212D – Climate and Earth science	AT1 Level 3 AT3 Level 3/4
71	What happens when?	To understand that changes occur when some solids are added to water.	It is intended that children actually make the mixes described so you will need suitable containers as well as the materials listed.	Science NC: Sc3 Changing materials; Separating mixtures of materials QCA: Unit 4D Solids, liquids and how they can be separated	SCN 212D – Climate and Earth science	AT1 Level 3 AT3 Level 3/4
72	Separate (2)	To understand that when solids do not dissolve or react with water they can be separated by filtering.	The term to be explained is 'filtering'. This is another experiment sheet requiring preparation and materials.	Science NC: Sc1 Ideas and evidence in science; Sc3 Separating mixtures of materials QCA: Unit 4D Solids, liquids and how they can be separated	SCN 212D – Climate and Earth science	AT1 Level 3 AT3 Level 3/4
73	Friction	To understand that the force between two moving surfaces is called friction. To group surfaces into high friction and low friction.	Where there is a maximum slide or lowest stick, such as with ice-skating, friction is lowest. The opposite is high friction.	Science NC: Sc4 Forces and motion QCA: Unit 4E Friction	SCN 222L – Forces and motion	AT4 Level 3/4
74	Friction and force meters	To use a force meter accurately. To learn that a newton is a unit of force. To understand that there is a force between an object and a surface that may prevent it from moving.	Nothing in the universe will move unless it is acted upon by a force (that is, something forces it to move). Force meters will be required for this activity.	Science NC: Sc1 Investigative skills; Sc4 Forces and motion QCA: Unit 4E Friction	SCN 222L – Forces and motion	AT1 Level 3 AT4 Level 3/4
75	Good conductors	To construct a circuit to test which materials let electricity flow through.	The terminology needs to be taught and the equipment provided. The test is, of course, self-marking.	Science NC: Sc3 Grouping and classifying materials; Sc4 Electricity QCA: Unit 4F Circuits and conductors	SCN 221J – Electricity	AT3 Level 3 AT4 Level 3
76	Making and breaking	To understand that a complete circuit is needed for a device to work. To understand that a switch can be used to make or break a circuit.	Touching corners 1 and 2 will complete the circuit; touching the others will not as the circuit will remain broken. Good equipment is essential. The maze can be constructed using strips of foil glued onto stiff card. Make sure that your glue works. The maze need not be as complicated as the one illustrated.	Science NC: Sc3 Grouping and classifying materials; Sc4 Electricity QCA: Unit 4F Circuits and conductors	SCN 220J – Electricity	AT3 Level 3 AT4 Level 3
77	Who was Henry VIII?	To identify features and characteristics of Henry VIII from a portrait.	You could investigate the picture as a class. What questions do the children want answered about the king's appearance? Excellent guidance on examining portraits can be gleaned from *A Teacher's Guide to Using Portraits*, by Susan Morris.	History NC: Historical enquiry; Britain and the wider world in Tudor times QCA: Unit 7 Why did Henry VIII marry six times?	SOC 204E – People, past events and societies	AT Level 3
78	Henry's queens	To know and use the names of the six wives of Henry VIII and put them in order.	Teach the mnemonic – 'divorced, beheaded, died; divorced, beheaded, survived'. Chant and cherish and never forget it. Use the dates as clues and start with the easiest ones, for example, Jane Seymour died 1537.	History NC: Chronological understanding; Britain and the wider world in Tudor times QCA: Unit 7 Why did Henry VIII marry six times?	SOC 204E – People, past events and societies	AT Level 3
79	Henry VIII: did and didn't	To learn about the role and duties of a Tudor monarch.	Children need to understand that the king had powers and duties and was always accompanied by courtiers. The king did most of the things listed except the mundane. He attended church regularly (he was head of the church), played sport as a young man (tennis) and had a reputation for musical composition.	History NC: Knowledge and understanding of events, people and changes in the past; Britain and the wider world in Tudor times QCA: Unit 7 Why did Henry VIII marry six times?	SOC 204E – People, past events and societies	AT Level 3

▲ **SCHOLASTIC** www.scholastic.co.uk

Page	Activity	Objectives	Teachers' notes	NC, QCA & Primary Framework	Curriculum for Excellence (Scotland)	AT links and levels
80	A comfortable house	To identify features of some Tudor buildings.	Stress that not all Tudor people lived in houses like this, partly this was a matter of wealth but also there was an imperative to use local building materials. Transporting heavy stone across the country was not an option for most people. Have ample reference material to hand for this sheet.	History NC: Historical enquiry; Britain and the wider world in Tudor times QCA: Unit 8 What were the differences between the lives of rich and poor people in Tudor times?	SOC 203C – People, past events and societies	AT Level 2
81	A list of clues	To use documentary evidence to draw inferences about the way some Tudor people lived.	This will pose reading problems because it has only been lightly edited. Approach the document as a problem-solving exercise. Point out the problems faced by historians when tackling documents.	History NC: Historical enquiry; Britain and the wider world in Tudor times QCA: Unit 8 What were the differences between the lives of rich and poor people in Tudor times?	SOC 201A – People, past events and societies	AT Level 3
82	The Second World War	To understand when and where the war took place and why it was called a 'world' war.	Children will already have some prior knowledge of this topic gleaned randomly from all sorts of sources. This sheet might be used as a way of establishing why it was called a 'world' war. Talk with the class about the contents of the sheet.	History NC: Historical enquiry; Britain since 1930 QCA: Unit 9 What was it like for children in the Second World War?	SOC 205E – People, past events and societies	AT Level 3
83	World War II timeline	To know the key events and dates of the Second World War.	Check that your children can cope with the numbers (dates) involved here. Reference books are essential. Don't stop at the 'cut and stick' exercise.	History NC: Chronological understanding; Britain since 1930 QCA: Unit 9 What was it like for children in the Second World War?	SOC 104E – People, past events and societies	AT Level 2
84	Evacuation	To understand why the strategy of evacuation was used to protect children during the Second World War.	The children should be used to investigating evidence before starting this sheet. *What is it? Where did it come from? Who made it? Why was it made?* As early as September 1938, plans were made for evacuation. The country was divided into areas; evacuation, neutral and reception. The government suggested that each child carry a bag containing a gas mask, change of underclothing, night clothes, house shoes, spare socks, toothbrush, comb, towel, soap, flannel, handkerchiefs and a coat.	History NC: Historical enquiry; Britain since 1930 QCA: Unit 9 What was it like for children in the Second World War?	SOC 205E – People, past events and societies	AT Level 2/3
85	Ancient Egypt: model behaviour	To make inferences and deductions from objects.	These funerary sculptures were made of wood, were carved and painted and were part of a set found on top of the coffin of a provincial governor, buried in a cave in the bank of the river Nile.	History NC: Historical enquiry; A world history study QCA: Unit 10 What can we find out about ancient Egypt…?	SOC 203C – People, past events and societies	AT Level 2/3
86	Land of the Nile	To locate Ancient Egypt on a historical map. To learn about its main geographical features.	This task could be tackled collectively, in small groups or in pairs.	History NC: Historical enquiry; A world history study QCA: Unit 10 What can we find out about ancient Egypt…?	SOC 203C – People, past events and societies	AT Level 2
87	What a load of rubbish!	To become aware of the amount of waste within the classroom. To collect and record evidence relating to this issue.	Discuss the issues raised here with the class. Look at the environmental problems around the school. Remember to make safe arrangements for handling the classroom waste produced.	Geography NC: Geographical enquiry and skills QCA: Unit 8 Improving the environment	SOC 208G – People, place and environment	AT Level 2
88	Settlements	To use maps to obtain evidence about settlements.	Make sure that children are reasonably secure in map reading. Can they recognise a river, for example? From the map, can the children suggest why settlements started where they did?	Geography NC: Geographical enquiry and skills; Knowledge and understanding of places QCA: Unit 9 Village settlers	SOC 214L – People, place and environment	AT Level 3
89	Where am I?	To use four-figure grid references accurately.	This sheet uses four-figure references only so children will be directed to a square not a precise point. This is an introduction to map reading. Children should begin working in pairs to test each other's skill. *Can you find what is in square 3294?* and so on.	Geography NC: Geographical enquiry and skills; Knowledge and understanding of places QCA: Unit 6 Investigating our local area	SOC 214L – People, place and environment	AT Level 3
90	From Britain to India	To use and interpret a world map. To locate India and the UK.	The final question is intended for open-ended discussion; definite answers are not expected.	Geography NC: Geographical enquiry and skills; Knowledge and understanding of places QCA: Unit 10 A village in India	SOC 212J – People, place and environment	AT Level 2/3

Page	Activity	Objectives	Teachers' notes	NC, QCA & Primary Framework	Curriculum for Excellence (Scotland)	AT links and levels
91	An Indian market	To identify features of a place from a resource. To use that resource to compare that place with the local area.	The photograph is of an Indian market in Calcutta. You could use an OHT of the picture with the whole class. Reference material will be required.	Geography NC: Geographical enquiry and skills; Breadth of study QCA: Unit 10 A village in India	SOC 212J – People, place and environment	AT Level 2/3
92	How do you spend your time?	To distinguish between work, leisure and recreation.	Clarify the categories: recreation usually involves activity and physical effort and generally takes place outside the home; leisure usually involves relaxation and may occur at home.	Geography NC: Geographical enquiry and skills QCA: Unit 19 How and where do we spend our time?	SOC 115M – People in society, economy and business	AT Level 3
93	How do you spend your time: a questionnaire	To devise a questionnaire.	Devising a questionnaire is not easy so tackle this sheet with the whole class. When the questionnaire has been completed individually, collate the results with the whole class.	Geography NC: Geographical enquiry and skills QCA: Unit 19 How and where do we spend our time?	SOC 115M; SOC 215M – People in society, economy and business	AT Level 3
94	Money in materials	To explore features of money container products To design a money container using textiles.	The answers have to be left open as, without handling the objects, it is impossible to be absolutely certain about the material from which they are made, but leather, cloth and plastic should be on the list. For the 'design and make' part of the activity, the children will need to select and obtain the materials.	Design and technology NC: Evaluating processes and products; Knowledge and understanding of materials and components QCA: Unit 4A Money containers	TCH 105C – Technologies SCN 115X – Properties and uses	AT Level 3
95	Sew a seam	To sew using a range of different stitches.	Management of the task in the classroom is very important as there are potential hazards in using needles.	Design and technology NC: Working with tools, equipment and materials QCA: Unit 4A Money containers	TCH 105C – Technologies EXA 108H; EXA 103C – Art and design SCN 115X – Properties and uses	AT Level 3
96	Controlling comic clown (1)	To investigate lever and linkage systems and to apply what they have learned.	A study of linkage-type mechanisms and a range of products with moving parts should precede the use of this sheet. Encourage the use of technical vocabulary: 'linkage', 'lever' and 'pivot'. The template provided on the sheet 'Controlling comic clown (2)' can be used to provide the basic structure so children can concentrate on designing the lever mechanism.	Design and technology NC: Knowledge and understanding of materials and components QCA: Unit 4B Storybooks	TCH 105C; TCH 107D – Technologies EXA 108H; EXA 103C – Art and design SCN 109L – Forces and motion	AT Level 2/3
97	Controlling comic clown (2)	To investigate lever and linkage systems and to apply what they have learned.	See the previous sheet 'Controlling comic clown (1)'.	Design and technology NC: Knowledge and understanding of materials and components QCA: Unit 4B Storybooks	TCH 105C; TCH 107D – Technologies EXA 108H; EXA 103C – Art and design SCN 109L – Forces and motion	AT Level 2/3
98	Are you switched on? (1)	To understand the way in which different types of switch can be activated.	This sheet and 'Are you switched on? (2)' are companions. They can be used in an 'examine and explain' way or as guides to practical work. The children should work in pairs. Note the foil is connected to the carton and is pulled by the string when it is tripped. This makes a connection that completes the circuit.	Design and technology NC: Working with tools, equipment, materials and components to make quality products; Knowledge and understanding of materials and components QCA: Unit 4E Lighting it up	TCH 107D – Technologies SCN 220J – Electricity	AT Level 3
99	Are you switched on? (2)	To understand the way in which different types of switch can be activated.	See the previous sheet. Rain water dissolves the sugar so the peg closes, the drawing pins touch, the circuit is completed and the alarm goes off.	Design and technology NC: Knowledge and understanding of materials and components QCA: Unit 4E Lighting it up	TCH 107D – Technologies SCN 220J – Electricity	AT Level 3
100	Alarming!	To apply what they have learned about switches. To construct an alarm.	This cannot be done without prior learning (see the preceding sheets 1 and 2).	Design and technology NC: Knowledge and understanding of materials and components; Developing and communicating ideas planning; Working with tools, equipment, materials and components QCA: Unit 4E Lighting it up	TCH 107D – Technologies SCN 220J – Electricity	AT Level 3
101	A place for colour	To recognise that ICT can be used to develop images.	This is a computer-based task requiring some ICT knowledge and skills. A suitable graphics package will be required, such as, Microsoft® Paint, as will a scanner.	ICT NC: Developing ideas and making things happen QCA: Unit 4B Developing images using repeating patterns	TCH 209E – Technologies	AT Level 2
102	Yes or no?	To create a series of yes/no questions in order to identify objects.	Discuss the exercise – 'yes' answers are more useful than 'no' answers. The task is only an introduction. Progress to using a tree diagram to identify more objects.	ICT NC: Finding things out; Developing ideas and making things happen QCA: Unit 4C Branching databases	TCH 213H – Technologies	AT Level 3/4

Page	Activity	Objectives	Teachers' notes	NC, QCA & Primary Framework	Curriculum for Excellence (Scotland)	AT links and levels
103	Graphs for a purpose	To learn that different graphs are used for different purposes. To use ICT to create a pie chart.	Long titles are the most accurate, such as 1. 'Vehicles travelling on a Sunday' 2. 'Vehicles travelling on a Monday'. 3. 'Monthly rainfall over a year'. 4. 'Growth of a child over four years'.	ICT NC: Finding things out QCA: Unit 4D Collecting and presenting information	TCH 213H – Technologies	AT Level 3/4
104	Turning turtle	To know that an on-screen turtle obeys the same commands as a floor turtle. To use repeat instruction and make predictions.	The children will need to be able to manipulate an on-screen 'turtle' (or similar).	ICT NC: Developing ideas and making things happen QCA: Unit 4E Modelling effects on screen	TCH 114J – Technologies	AT Level 3/4
105	Varying viewpoints	To find and record interesting and different viewpoints.	The illustrations are there as guidance only. Let children explore the environment in the ways suggested and to make a collection of sketches. A choice of sketching pencils should be provided.	Art and design NC: Exploring and developing ideas QCA: Unit 4A Viewpoints	EXA 005E – Art and design	AT Level 3
106	Collograph	To select an image and develop a design for a print.	A 'collograph' is a card block print and creating one is a good 'investigate and make' activity. It is recommended that you use water-based inks that can be cleaned up fairly easily (you have been warned).	Art and design NC: Exploring and developing ideas; Investigating and making art, craft and design; Knowledge and understanding QCA: Unit 4A Viewpoints	EXA 206E – Art and design	AT Level 2/3
107	Dream art	To develop designs using what they have learned from the study of other artists.	You may wish to show children more photographs that have a dream-like quality before setting the task. The challenge is to develop a print design on the 'dream' theme using printing skills (see the previous sheet).	Art and design NC: Exploring and developing ideas; Investigating and making art, craft and design; Knowledge and understanding QCA: Unit 4A Viewpoints	EXA 106F – Art and design	AT Level 3
108	Choose a chair	To explore ideas about chairs. To design a chair to suit a particular unusual character.	A good way to confront this task is in groups with an appointed 'scribe' to record findings. The 'unusual' character could be real or fictional, for example, The Iron Man, or Gromit.	Art and design NC: Exploring and developing ideas; Investigating and making art, craft and design; Breadth of study QCA: Unit 4B Take a seat	EXA 101A – Art and design	AT Level 3
109	Take five: the pentatonic scale	To play ostinati based upon the pentatonic scale.	Play the repeating patterns counting three or four beats in the bar as shown. Children should use two hands when playing with beaters holding lightly. Any combination of notes in the pentatonic scale can be played without undue tonal clashing.	Music NC: Controlling sounds through singing and playing; Listening, applying knowledge and understanding QCA: Unit 12 Dragon scales	EXA 113Q – Music	AT Level 3
110	Take five into the forest	To compose a simple melody and accompaniment using the pentatonic scale.	This uses the pentatonic scale in F (FGACD).	Music NC: Controlling sounds through singing and playing; Creating and developing musical ideas QCA: Unit 12 Dragon scales	EXA 113Q – Music	AT Level 3
111	Mood music	To create sounds which describe moods or emotions.	The picture on the sheet is *Island in the Sound* by Albert Bierstadt. Talk about the activity. *How do colour and texture in art relate to musical colours?*	Music NC: Responding and reviewing; Creating and developing musical ideas QCA: Unit 13 Painting with sound	EXA 214Q – Music	AT Level 2/3
112	Sounds and pictures	To create sounds that tell the story of a picture.	In this case the picture tells a story so the music that is created needs to have a narrative element in it. This should be a cooperative activity.	Music NC: Responding and reviewing; Creating and developing musical ideas QCA: Unit 13 Painting with sound	EXA 214Q – Music	AT Level 2/3
113	Game for a song (1)	To sing and play a range of singing games.	Children should first have discussed and performed a range of singing games. Games are not easily pigeon-holed but try to find some in the categories listed on the sheet. Children will need ample space to play the games.	Music NC: Controlling sounds through singing and playing; Creating and developing musical ideas; Responding and reviewing QCA: Unit 14 Salt, pepper, vinegar, mustard	EXA 011Q – Music	AT Level 2/3
114	Game for a song (2)	To sing and play a range of singing games.	The words and rhythm point to this being a skipping game but if children devise a fitting alternative then so be it.	Music NC: Controlling sounds through singing and playing; Listening, and applying knowledge and understanding QCA: Unit 14 Salt, pepper, vinegar, mustard	EXA 215S – Music	AT Level 3/4

Page	Activity	Objectives	Teachers' notes	NC, QCA & Primary Framework	Curriculum for Excellence (Scotland)	AT links and levels
115	Aum	To learn and recognise the aum symbol and understand its significance to Hindus.	Set this sheet in the context of a study of Hindu worship. Introduce the children to the Hindu notion of one god in many forms. Hindus respect the shrines and images of the particular form of god they choose to worship but each deity is ultimately the personification of Brahman, the ultimate Supreme Being.	RE Non-statutory framework: Learning about religion; Breadth of study (Religions and beliefs)		Non-statutory AT1 Level 2
116	Where is God? A Hindu story	To reflect upon a Hindu way of expressing belief about the nature of God.	The order is: 1. What do you know about God? 2. Bring salt and water. 3. Put the salt in the glass. 4. The next day. 5. Taste the water. 6. God is like that salt. Talk should follow the task.	RE Non-statutory framework: Learning about religion; Breadth of study (Religions and beliefs)		Non-statutory AT1 Level 2/3
117	How far is it to Bethlehem?	To understand the significance of Bethlehem for Christians.	Atlases are required as well as a good knowledge of the Christmas story.	RE Non-statutory framework: Learning about religion; Breadth of study (Religions and beliefs)		Non-statutory AT1 Level 2/3
118	A Christmas carol	To understand how carols and music are used to celebrate the Christmas story.	Making up additional verses to the tune 'Here we go round the mulberry bush' is not difficult, for example, 'Jesus was born in Bethlehem'.	RE Non-statutory framework: Learning about religion; Breadth of study (Religions and beliefs)		Non-statutory AT1 Level 2
119	The Easter story (1): Palm Sunday	To learn the story of Palm Sunday.	A calendar showing the Easter dates would be useful. Bibles are also required. Different versions of the story can help with detective work and discussion.	RE Non-statutory framework: Learning about religion; Breadth of study (Religions and beliefs)		Non-statutory AT1 Level 2/3
120	The Easter story (2): the Last Supper	To know the story of the Last Supper and to understand what the Eucharist is.	If the children know little of the story, let them do some detective work. The latter part of the sheet might best be explained by a practising Christian. A visit to a local church is worthwhile. Explore www.culham.ac.uk for ideas.	RE Non-statutory framework: Learning about religion; Breadth of study (Religions and beliefs)		Non-statutory AT1 Level 2/3
121	The Easter story (3)	To learn the main events of the story of the crucifixion and resurrection.	The pictures tell the story in outline only and you can fill in as much detail as you feel the children are able to cope with. Discuss with the class the symbolism of the cross.	RE Non-statutory framework: Learning about religion; Breadth of study (Religions and beliefs)		Non-statutory AT1 Level 2/3
122	Rules and laws protect us (1)	To understand that rules and laws are designed to protect us.	The explanations need only be in general terms. The answers to the *how?* question should embody common-sense principles. One way of tackling why an act is wrong is to examine the reverse scenario, such as, *What would happen if there were no traffic laws?*	PSHE and Citizenship NC guidelines: Preparing to play an active role as citizens QCA: Unit 8 How do rules and laws affect me?		N/A
123	Rules and laws protect us (2)	To understand that rules and laws are designed to protect us.	Make the point that although rules are needed to protect the weak and vulnerable, they are needed to protect the strong too.	PSHE and Citizenship NC guidelines: Preparing to play an active role as citizens QCA: Unit 8 How do rules and laws affect me?		N/A
124	Community connections	To be aware of the variety of communities to which we belong simultaneously.	Define the term 'community' simply as a 'group'. The central ring has been left empty. The children can draw or place a photograph of themselves at the centre of their world.	PSHE and Citizenship NC guidelines: Developing good relationships…. QCA: Unit 5 Living in a diverse world		N/A
125	Heroes and heroines	To recognise and explore feelings about some role models for young people.	Distinguish between a quality such as *loyalty*, that involves an admirable action and one such as *being tall*, that does not. Children will learn that moral issues are not always straightforward. A despicable person may be a brilliant footballer.	PSHE and Citizenship NC guidelines: Developing good relationships and respecting the differences between people		N/A
126	In other people's shoes	To be able to put themselves into someone else's shoes.	The exercise is not as easy as it looks. Children need to think about the issues involved – Dad's life may seem very easy from the child's point of view but may actually be very hard.	PSHE and Citizenship NC guidelines: Developing good relationships and respecting the differences between people		N/A
127	What we do for each other	To develop a concern for other people. To appreciate the importance of taking responsibility for their behaviour.	Children may appreciate that Mum makes their sandwiches, but may be less sensitive to the fact that she also comforts them when distressed, gives them love and attention and so on.	PSHE and Citizenship NC guidelines: Developing good relationships…. QCA: Unit 4 People who help us – the local police		N/A

NO FUSS
PHOTOCOPIABLE

SCHOLASTIC
www.scholastic.co.uk

Words containing 'k'

● Add some words of your own to each group. Use a dictionary.
● Do you notice any patterns in each group?

:) end

suck
hawk
whisk
unlock

lipstick
wink
back
thick

:) middle

trinket
bike
lake
buckle
ducked
luckily
bucket

:) beginning

kick
knife
kipper
kite
kill
keyboard

Name _____

Words ending in 'y'

● Use these words to make new words to fit in either list **A** or list **B**.

stray	fry	pray	carry
stay		play	hurry
try	empty	enjoy	cry

A

_____ s

_____ s

_____ s

_____ s

_____ s

_____ s

_____ s

_____ s

B

_____ ies

_____ ies

_____ ies

_____ ies

_____ ies

_____ ies

_____ ies

_____ ies

● Can you see a pattern in each list?
● Think of some more words to add to the lists.

One of our consonants is missing!

● You should be seeing double in these words but one of the consonants is missing.
● Which one? Spell the word correctly three times and remember the spelling. Cross out the wrongly spelled words!

puzle →	puzzle	puzzle	puzzle
woble →			
buton →			
colar →			
miten →			
nible →			
misile →			
netle →			
mesage →			
jely →			
geting →			
hamer →			
puting →			
leson →			
batle →			

Adding 'ing' to verbs

- ● Link these words in pairs. The first one is done for you.
- ● If the last consonant is doubled, colour the pair in **red**.
- ● If the last 'e' is dropped, colour the pair in **yellow**.
- ● If there is no change, colour the pair in **blue**.

Tagged on the end: suffixes

● Use the suffixes **hood**, **al**, **ary**, **ship** and **ness** to make new words from this list.

critic	_____	craftsman	_____
neighbour	_____	father	_____
station	_____	sad	_____
member	_____	cheerful	_____
diction	_____	second	_____
fiction	_____	leader	_____
mother	_____	herb	_____
dictator	_____	department	_____

● Can you write any other words that have these suffixes?

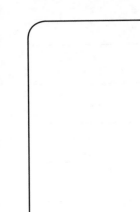

Name _____

Finding adverbs

Find five adverbs to finish each of these people's sentences. An example has been done for you in each speech bubble.

Well Gary, I think that the players passed the ball **accurately**.

_____
_____
_____
_____
_____

In Wales the wind will blow **ferociously**.

_____
_____
_____
_____

I finished my homework **swiftly**.

MATHS
KEVIN ROGERS

_____
_____
_____
_____
_____

Homophones

Choose the correct word from the brackets to fill the gaps.

1. There are _____ green bottles hanging on the wall. What are they _____? (for, four)

2. There are _____ more green bottles in the fridge. I must go _____ the supermarket _____ get four more. You can come _____. (to, too, two)

3. Green bottles are all _____ selling, _____ shelves are full of them but _____ is another bottle shop in Bognor. (their, there, they're)

4. How can I carry these bottles all the _____ home? They _____ too much. (weigh, way)

5. Can you _____ what I am saying? They only sell green bottles _____. (here, hear)

6. Bottles to the left, bottles to the _____ , there are bottles everywhere. I will _____ a letter to the manager and complain. (write, right)

7. A _____ shop in the High Street sells blue bottles. I _____ that someone would sell a different colour. (knew, new)

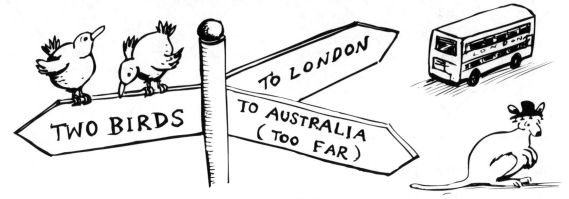

Name _____

The tense connection

● Join the present tense verb to its past tense. You will find it inside the same shape.

Present tense verb	Past tense verb

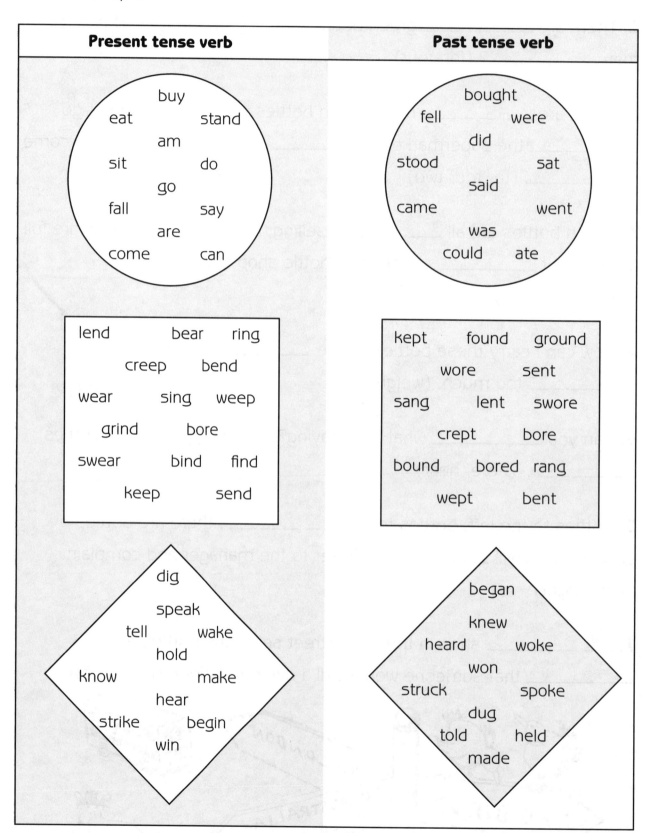

Present tense verb

buy
eat   stand
am
sit   do
go
fall   say
are
come   can

lend   bear   ring
creep   bend
wear   sing   weep
grind   bore
swear   bind   find
keep   send

dig
speak
tell   wake
hold
know   make
hear
strike   begin
win

Past tense verb

bought
fell   were
did
stood   sat
said
came   went
was
could   ate

kept   found   ground
wore   sent
sang   lent   swore
crept   bore
bound   bored   rang
wept   bent

began
knew
heard   woke
won
struck   spoke
dug
told   held
made

● Investigate the pairs of words.

Belongs to...

Follow the examples and add the apostrophes to the sentences.

> **Rule 1:** Apostrophes can be used to show that something belongs to someone or something:
>
> The donkey**'s** tail was long and furry.

1. The maid polished the queens crown.

2. Arthurs seat was painted green.

3. The blackbirds stomach was full of cherries.

Watch out! Not every **s** at the end of a word means 'belongs to'.

> **Rule 2:** If the word is a plural ending in **s**, then the apostrophe goes after the **s**:
>
> The bird**s'** nests were full of eggs.

4. Most of the soldiers guns were clean.

5. The chairs covers had been faded by the sun.

6. The girls tongues were poking out at the boys.

> **Rule 3:** If the word is a plural not ending in **s**, then the apostrophe comes before the added **s**:
>
> The women**'s** hats blew off.

7. The cat ate all the childrens dinners.

8. During the song, the mens voices could be heard above the sound of the trumpets.

9. He cut off the sheeps tails with scissors.

Name _____

Its or it's?

The donkey flapped **its** ears. → no apostrophe

It's raining. → apostrophe 's'

Use **its** or **it's** to fill the blanks in these sentences.

(REMEMBER if you can replace **its** with **it is** then it should be **it's**.
If you can't then **its** is correct.)

1. Hamlet the cat chewed _____ tail.

2. Put your coats on children, _____ raining outside.

3. _____ a long way to Tipperary.

4. I think _____ the first time Swindon have been in the Cup Final.

5. Don't wear that tie with that shirt, _____ green.

6. The helicopter dipped _____ nose and then sped away.

7. _____ brown with crust around _____ edges. What is it?

8. In Grimsby _____ easy to buy fish and chips.

9. In Australia _____ easy to get sunburnt.

10. _____ Sunday and _____ raining. A bird shakes _____ wet
wings and flies to the highest branch of the tree.

Punctuation marks

● Punctuation helps a reader make sense of writing. Do you know these marks? Link them to their correct names.

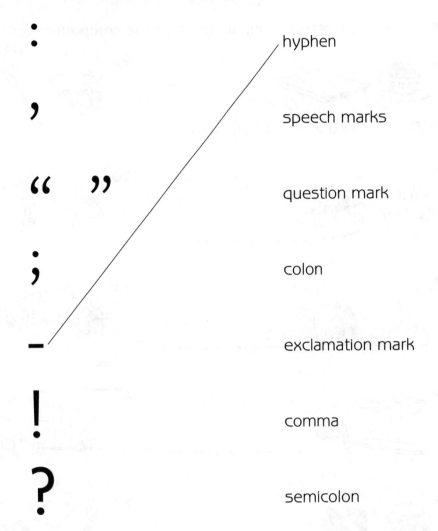

:

,

" "

;

–

!

?

hyphen

speech marks

question mark

colon

exclamation mark

comma

semicolon

● Underline all the punctuation marks in this writing. How many of each are there?

Tim has served an ace! Is this his big chance? Hackforth-Jones is waiting for Tim's next serve. Will it be another ace? Jones has tried his best all through the match, but his best might not be good enough today. Just a minute! The umpire is making an announcement.

"Ladies and gentlemen, the game is abandoned due to poor light."

Can you believe that? We have had everything today: rain, snow, wind, a duck on court and now bad light! The crowd is very angry. People are throwing cushions, hats, programmes and ice creams at the umpire. The players have gone, so I think it's all over. Oh dear, here comes the rain; so it is now.

Name _____

Compound words

● Look at the pictures and write down the **compound** words.

1.

cup   board <u> cupboard </u>

9.

_____

2.

_____

10.

_____

3.

_____

11.

_____

4.

_____

12.

_____

5.

_____

13.

_____

6.

_____

14.

_____

7.

_____

15.

_____

8.

_____

16.

_____

● Use your dictionary to find some more compound words.

NO FUSS
PHOTOCOPIABLE

SCHOLASTIC
www.scholastic.co.uk

Name _____

Poem parts

● Use your dictionary to find the meanings of these words:

verse _____

chorus _____

rhyming couplet _____

stanza _____

● Read the poem. Underline a verse in red, a chorus in blue, a stanza in yellow and a couplet in green.

The Jumblies

They went to sea in a Sieve, they did,
In a Sieve they went to sea:
In spite of all their friends could say,
On a winter's morn, on a stormy day,
In a Sieve they went to sea!
And when the Sieve turned round and round,
And every one cried, 'You'll all be drowned!'
They called aloud, 'Our Sieve ain't big,
But we don't care a button! we don't care a fig!
In a Sieve we'll go to sea!'
Far and few, far and few,
Are the lands where the Jumblies live;
Their heads are green, and their hands are blue,
And they went to sea in a Sieve.

They sailed away in a Sieve, they did,
In a Sieve they sailed so fast,
With only a beautiful pea-green veil
Tied with a riband by way of a sail,
To a small tobacco-pipe mast;
And every one said, who saw them go,
'O won't they be soon upset, you know!
For the sky is dark, and the voyage is long,
And happen what may, it's extremely wrong
In a Sieve to sail so fast!'
Far and few, far and few,
Are the lands where the Jumblies live;
Their heads are green, and their hands are blue,
And they went to sea in a Sieve.

Edward Lear

Name _____

Points of view

Here are some arguments in favour of cycling as a form of transport. Choose the best points and put them into a letter to the local newspaper. Start 'Dear Editor...'

Cycling helps to keep you fit.

Cycling is often quicker than going by car in cities.

Bicycles are quieter than cars.

Cycling is cheaper than any other form of transport.

Bicycles don't need expensive motorways.

Bicycles take up less room than cars.

Cycling is a good way to see the countryside because it is slower than driving.

You don't have to pay tax to ride a bicycle.

Cycling does not cause pollution.

You can get to places by bicycle that a car cannot get to.

You don't need a large garage for a bicycle.

NO FUSS PHOTOCOPIABLE

Purr-suasion

Questions below the advertisement:

- How is this product being sold?
- What ways has the advertiser used to attract buyers?
- What is your opinion of this advertisement?
- Design an advertisement of your own using similar tactics.

Name _____

Making a new ending

The woodcutter arrived in the nick of time and killed the wolf.
Little Red Riding Hood was saved.

Use the frames below to write a different ending.

The woodcutter arrived at the cottage

Then

But

Finally

Writing up notes

PC 49

9:00pm	Stopped to investigate ringing alarm at fish shop.
9:05pm	Mr Kadar arrived to switch off alarm. Car passed at high speed. Gave chase.
9:15pm	Car identified as red Ford. Stopped in Long Street. Chased on foot.
9:20pm	Cornered suspects by post office. I was attacked with stick. Arrested 1 man. Other escaped.
9:21pm	Called for reinforcements.
9:30pm	Police van arrived. Searched alleys. Found stolen mobile phones in dustbin.
9:50pm	Lucy (police dog) found other suspect in garden shed. Suspect kicked dog. Lucy unhurt but man bitten on rear end. All cuffed and collected.
10:00pm	Returned to patrol.

Use the notes from the police notebook to write a full report of the crime.

_____

_____

_____

_____

_____

_____

_____

_____

_____

Edit this

Use a red pen or pencil to edit this passage down so that it is more precise. Cross out repetitions and unnecessary information.

There was a knock at the door. Brian opened it because I was putting my lipstick on. I'd just bought a new colour, *Fungus Green.* Anyway, when he opened the door he found a group of excited people in the garden.

"Do you own a dog?" asked one of the women.

They were very excited.

"Yes," said Brian, "although we don't really own the dog we are just looking after it while our son Stephen is away on holiday. He has gone to Blackpool."

They were very excited.

"There's been an accident," a man said.

They were all so excited. We rushed outside. There was the poor dog whimpering in the road, but it seemed all right. I noticed she was wearing the collar I bought for her last Christmas. They were still very excited. Two women were running up and down the road crying.

"It has lost a leg!" one of the women cried. "Can you find it?"

Brian tried to calm her down. They were all very excited.

"It only had three legs to start with," he said.

After that we took the dog indoors and counted its legs, just to make sure, then it ate some jelly. It seemed OK.

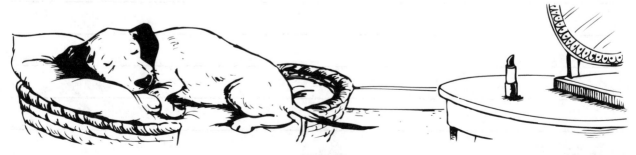

NO FUSS
PHOTOCOPIABLE

A simile poem

● Complete these **similes**. Look at the pictures for clues to the missing words.

He fled from the room…

…like a _____ in a rage,

…like a _____ in a battle,

…like a _____ in a stampede,

…like a _____ from a gun.

● Use your own ideas to complete this poem. You can add some more verses of your own.

The old man was…

…as wise as a _____,

…as proud as a _____,

…as hairy as a _____,

…as brave as a _____,

…as bold as a _____.

Name _____

Groups of adjectives

● Put these **adjectives** into sets that have similar meanings.

happy	chilly	secure	content	wild
protected	mad	furious	freezing	unharmed
satisfied	bitter	livid	cool	frosty

pleased

angry

cold

safe

● Use a **thesaurus** to add to these groups.

warm

cautious

■ SCHOLASTIC
www.scholastic.co.uk

Placing adverbs

HOW?
merrily
happily
swiftly
roughly
firmly
carefully

WHERE?
nowhere
there
here
everywhere

WHEN?
tomorrow
earlier
later
yesterday

Write sentences that each contain at least one of the adverbs from the sets above.

Name _____

What would you have done?

If you had been Goldilocks…

What would you have done on entering the house?

What would you have done next?

How do you think the story should end?

Words and numbers

● Make the biggest number you can using all these digits.

   6   1   5   4   3   _____

Make the smallest number using the same digits. _____

Write the smallest number in words.

_____

● Do the same using these digits.

   2   0   4   5   3

Biggest number   _____

Smallest number   _____

Smallest number in words _____

● Put the correct numbers in the boxes.

6531 = [   ] + 500 + 30 + 1

1786 = 1000 + [   ] + 80 + 6

4932 = 4000 + 900 + [   ] + 2

5811 = 5000 + 800 + 10 + [   ]

7634 = [   ] + 600 + 30 = 4

Name _____

Approximate

● Round these measurements to the nearest 10.

36kg   _____

437m   _____

42 miles   _____

25l   _____

2364 miles   _____

31 minutes   _____

● Round these numbers to the nearest 100.

537   _____

493   _____

1631   _____

97   _____

876   _____

9430   _____

● Put a circle round the best approximation for:

18 x 5	80 x 6	8 x 60	88 x 5	20 x 5
703 + 196	700 + 200	700 + 100	800 + 200	
49 x 19	40 x 10	50 x 10	40 x 20	50 x 20

Name _____

Negative integers

A **whole number** is called an **integer**.

● Number lines can go in two directions. Fill in the missing integers on this line.

–6   –2   –1   0   1   2   5

● What is the temperature on this thermometer?

● Use a coloured pencil and a ruler to complete this diagram showing **subtract 3**. Start on the left number line. Keep going until you run out of number line!

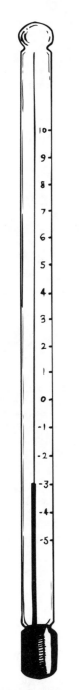

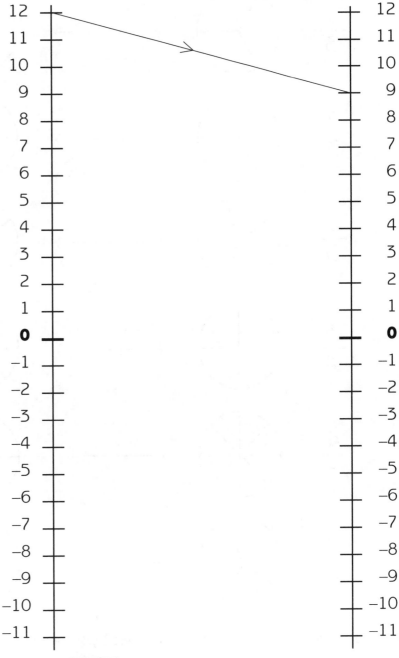

Name _____

Equivalent fractions (1)

● Colour in the equivalent fraction and write its name. The first one is done for you.

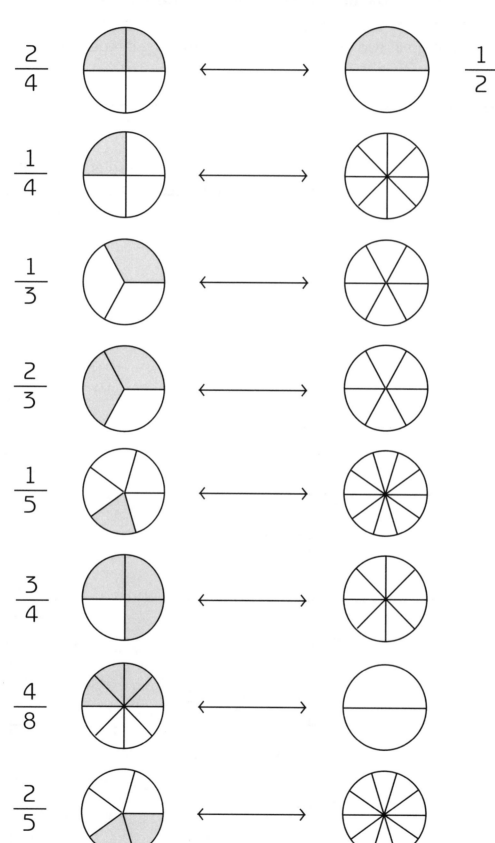

$\dfrac{2}{4}$ ⟷ $\dfrac{1}{2}$

$\dfrac{1}{4}$ ⟷

$\dfrac{1}{3}$ ⟷

$\dfrac{2}{3}$ ⟷

$\dfrac{1}{5}$ ⟷

$\dfrac{3}{4}$ ⟷

$\dfrac{4}{8}$ ⟷

$\dfrac{2}{5}$ ⟷

● Learn these equivalent fractions. Test your memory with a friend.

■SCHOLASTIC
www.scholastic.co.uk

Equivalent fractions (2)

● Work out these equivalent fractions.

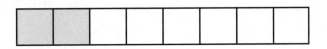

$\frac{2}{8}$ shaded → $\frac{}{4}$

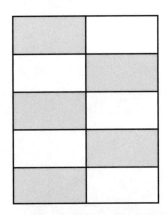

$\frac{5}{10}$ shaded → $\frac{}{4}$

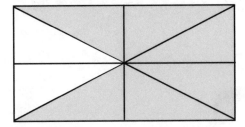

$\frac{3}{4}$ shaded → $\frac{}{8}$

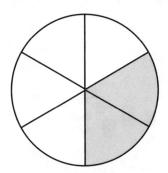

$\frac{2}{6}$ shaded → $\frac{}{3}$

● Shade the following fractions.

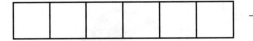 $\frac{1}{2}$

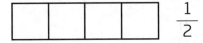 $\frac{2}{3}$

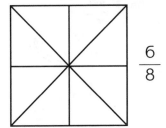 $\frac{6}{8}$

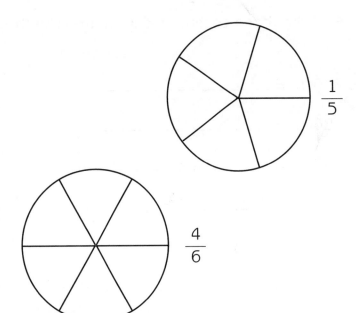

$\frac{1}{5}$

$\frac{4}{6}$

Name _____

Decimal places

- Put these decimals in the right places on the number line above.

2.5
2.8
0.7
1.6
0.4
1.3

- Write these amounts of money in pounds like this: 365p = £3.65

452p = _____

222p = _____

1736p = _____

525p = _____

694p = _____

962p = _____

- Write these centimetres in metres like this: 359cm = 3.59m

236cm = _____

486cm = _____

132cm = _____

26cm = _____

9232cm = _____

411cm = _____

PHOTOCOPIABLE

Check it out!

We can check calculations by the following methods:

A 321 – 45 = 276   CHECK   276 + 45 = $\boxed{321}$ ✔

B 30 × 5 = 150   CHECK   150 ÷ 5 = $\boxed{30}$ ✔

● Use method **A** or **B** to check these calculations.
  (Watch out! They are not all correct!)

465 – 82 = 383   CHECK → _____

91 – 28 = 63   CHECK → _____

25 × 6 = 150   CHECK → _____

12 × 8 = 88   CHECK → _____

40 × 4 = 160   CHECK → _____

633 – 66 = 566   CHECK → _____

● How would you check the following?

158 + 37 = 195   CHECK → _____

524 + 125 = 651   CHECK → _____

120 ÷ 4 = 30   CHECK → _____

32 ÷ 2 = 16   CHECK → _____

NO FUSS
PHOTOCOPIABLE

Name _____

Number problems

● A spider has 8 legs.
Daniel keeps 13 spiders as pets.
How many legs altogether?

_____

● Ruth loves chocolate biscuits.
There are 36 in the barrel. She eats 5 on Monday and the same number every day until there are none left. On what day does she finish the last one?

_____

● 5 people live in Eve's house.
They all take 3 spoonfuls of sugar in their tea, except Eve who takes only one.
How many spoonfuls for the whole family when they all drink tea?

_____

● Half of Delilah's class were born in Israel, a quarter were born in Ireland, the rest were born in Hendon.
There are 32 in the class.
How many were not born in Hendon?

_____

● Jezebel adds 16 to a number and gets 33.
What number did she start with?

_____

Put it another way

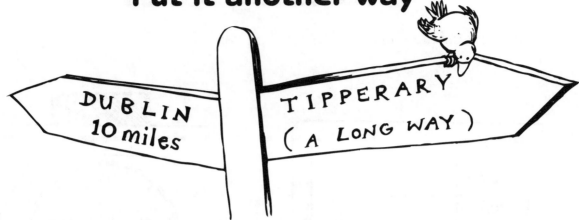

Learn and remember:

1 metre = 100 centimetres

1 kilometre = 1000 metres

1 kilogram = 1000 grams

1 litre = 1000 millilitres

Write these measurements another way.

1. 5322 grams = _____5_____ kilograms _____322_____ grams

2. 2129 grams = _____ kilograms _____ grams

3. 9003 grams = _____ kilograms _____ grams

4. 10042 grams = _____ kilograms _____ grams

5. 2.26 metres = _____ metres _____ centimetres

6. 5.72 metres = _____ metres _____ centimetres

7. 14.35 metres = _____ metres _____ centimetres

8. 9.04 metres = _____ metres _____ centimetres

9. 2467 millilitres = _____ litres _____ millilitres

10. 1324 millilitres = _____ litres _____ millilitres

11. 5100 millilitres = _____ litres _____ millilitres

12. 6008 millilitres = _____ litres _____ millilitres

Learn and remember:

1 mile is longer than 1 kilometre but less than 2 kilometres.

Measuring scales

Read these measures as accurately as you can.

1.

2.

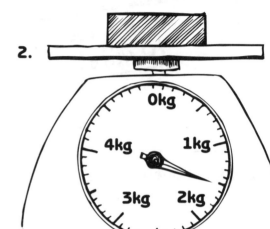

3.

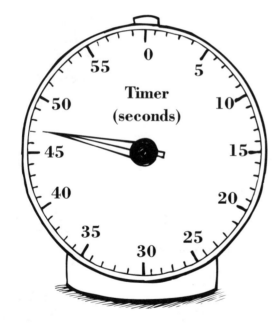

4.

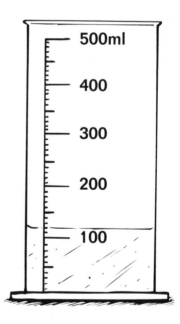

5.

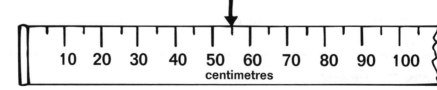

NO
FUSS
PHOTOCOPIABLE

■SCHOLASTIC
www.scholastic.co.uk

Journey round the edge: perimeter

● Draw round each of these shapes with a coloured pencil.
● Measure how far your pencil travelled in each case.

1.

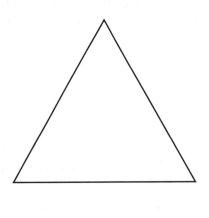

_____

2.

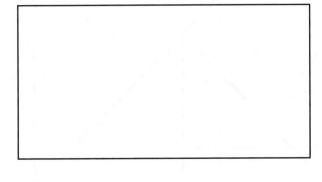

_____

3.

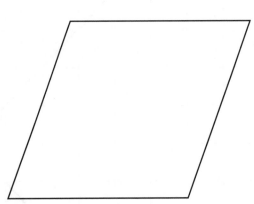

_____

4.

_____

5.

_____

Name _____

Tangram

● What is the area of this square? _____

● This is a Chinese puzzle called a **tangram**. Colour the pieces and cut them out. Rearrange them to make interesting shapes. What area does your new shape have?

_____

● Can you put the square back together again?

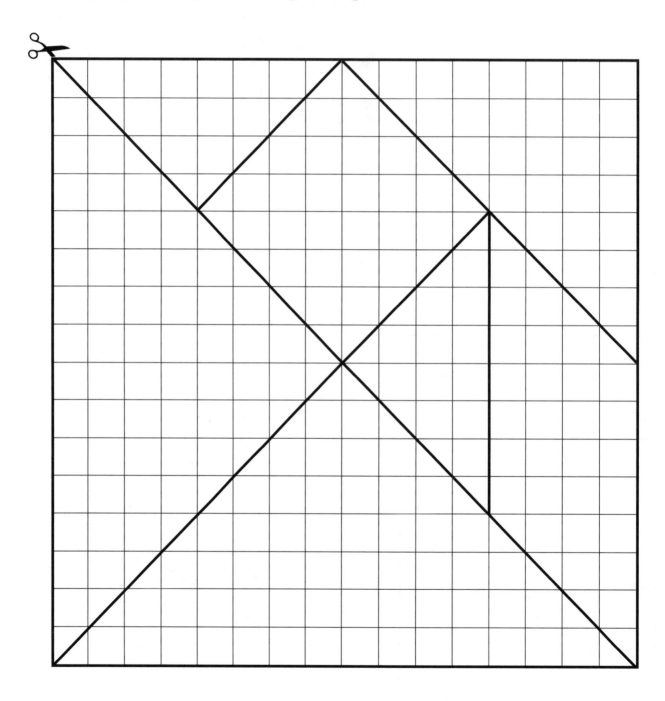

■ SCHOLASTIC
www.scholastic.co.uk

Name _____

Make a date

Recite and learn this rhyme about the number of days in each month of the year.

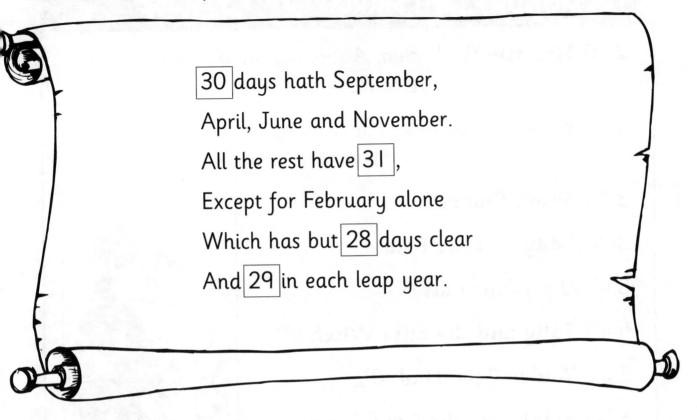

30 days hath September,

April, June and November.

All the rest have 31 ,

Except for February alone

Which has but 28 days clear

And 29 in each leap year.

1. How many days in June? _____

2. How many days in March? _____

3. How many days in December? _____

4. How many days in February in a leap year? _____

5. How many days in February this year? _____

6. Write down the day, month and year of your birthday.

_____

7. If September 1st is a Monday, what day is September 7th? _____

and what day is the last day in September? _____

8. December 15th is a Monday. What day is Christmas Day? _____

Time for TV

TV MONDAY 12TH MARCH

2:10 Heartthrob *Drama. A robbery brings love to PC 49. (R)*

3:10 News Headlines *Followed by regional news and weather.*

3:20 Small Planets

3:30 Eddy and the Bear

3:45 Ugly Martians *(R)*

4:40 Sally and the Silly Witch *(R)*

5:05 You've Been Had! *(R)*

5:30 Relatives *Brad and Sheila have an argument.*

6:00 News and Weather.

1. How long does *Heartthrob* last? _____

2. How long from the end of *Small Planets* to the start of *Sally and the Silly Witch*?

_____

3. Which is the longer programme, *You've Been Had!* or *Relatives*?

_____

4. If *Heartthrob* lasted 12 minutes longer than planned, what time would it finish?

_____

5. If you watched all of these programmes, for how long would you have

watched TV? _____

NO FUSS PHOTOCOPIABLE

Name _____

Put Polly in a polygon

Here is Polly in a polygon. A **polygon** is a flat shape with at least 3 straight sides. This polygon is a **quadrilateral**.

● Draw Polly inside these polygons and write the name of each polygon underneath:

a square   a heptagon   an equilateral triangle

a rectangle   a hexagon   a pentagon

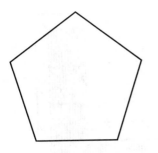

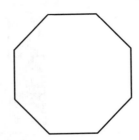

_____

_____

_____

_____

_____

_____

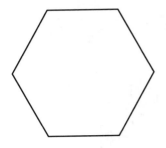

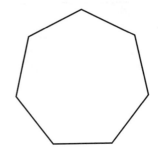

_____

_____

_____

Building with cubes

● Look at these drawings. What is the least number of cubes needed to build these models?

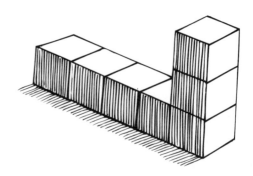

1. Number of cubes _____

2. Number of cubes _____

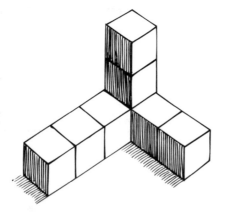

3. Number of cubes _____

4. Number of cubes _____

● Estimate how many cubes you would need to build this model. _____

● Build it and check your estimate.

● What is the difference?

_____

Name _____

Ordered pairs

● Two numbers are used to describe a point on a grid. Look carefully and notice which number comes first.

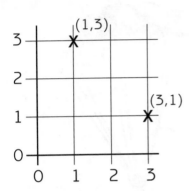

Remember we go in the door

before going up the stairs.

● Use pairs of numbers (in the correct order) to describe the points labelled A to L. Write your answers by the points on the grid.

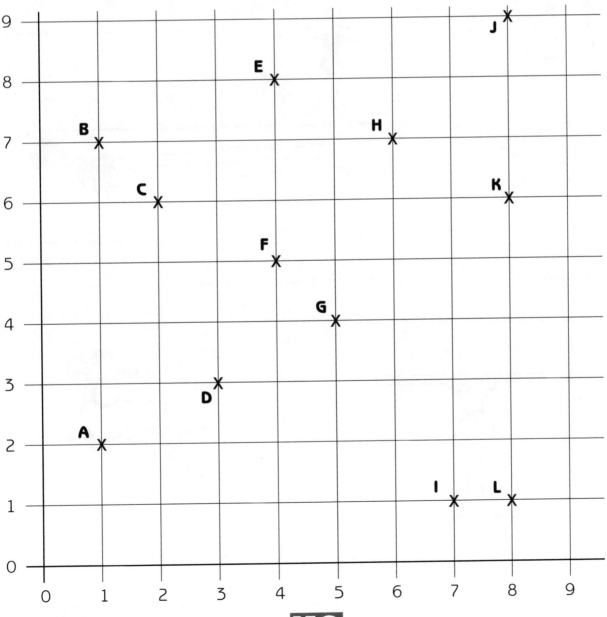

Name _____

Horizontal and vertical

Which is which? Write the correct word by each picture.
Is the object **horizontal** or **vertical**?

The plane is _____

The parachutist is

_____

The balance beam is _____

The flagpole is

_____

The girl is _____

The table top is _____

The water is

The table leg is _____

_____

Sizing up angles

Put these sets of angles in size order, starting with the smallest.

1.

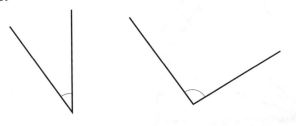 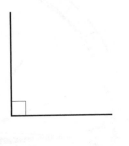 

A   B   C   D

Size order _____

2.

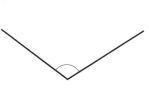  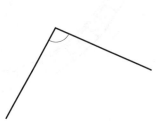 

A   B   C   D

Size order _____

3.

  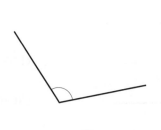 

A   B   C   D

Size order _____

4.

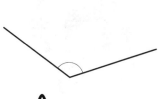 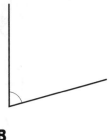  

A   B   C   D

Size order _____

Name _____

A question of degrees

● If you were facing **due east**, how many degrees would you turn through to face (by the shortest route):

south _____   direction of turn _____

north east _____   direction of turn _____

north _____   direction of turn _____

south east _____   direction of turn _____

● Face **north**. Turn **clockwise** to face the following directions. How many degrees do you turn through?

east _____

south _____

west _____

north (again) _____

south east _____

north west _____

Name _____

Sort by sets

● Add these to the diagram:
51, 54, 33, 27, 41, 58, 50, 53

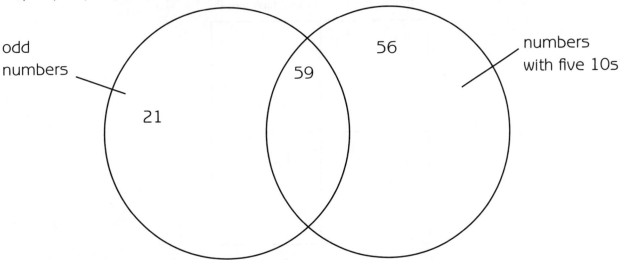

odd
numbers

56

59

21

numbers
with five 10s

● Add these to the diagram:
8, 20, 15, 25, 45, 60, 35

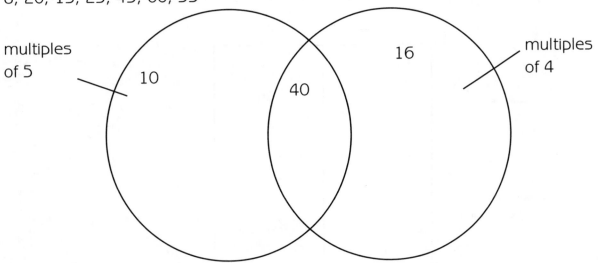

multiples
of 5

16

10

40

multiples
of 4

● Add these to the diagram:
30, 25, 9, 27, 45, 18, 40

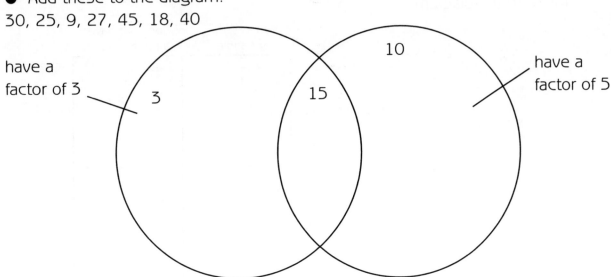

have a
factor of 3

10

3

15

have a
factor of 5

**NO
FUSS**
PHOTOCOPIABLE

Name _____

Get sorted!

● Add these to the diagram: 6, 27, 9, 17, 1, 25, 2, 12, 16, 20, 23

	multiples of 2	not multiples of 2
multiples of 3	24 30	3 21
not multiples of 3	4 26	19 5

● Add these to the diagram: 40, 47, 21, 44, 26, 45, 48, 27, 31, 36

	odd	even
numbers that have four 10s	41	46
numbers that do not have four 10s	33	28

● Add these to the diagram:

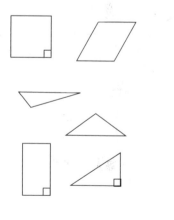

	has a right angle	does not have a right angle
has four sides		
does not have four sides		

Name _____

The human skeleton

Humans and other animals have bony skeletons inside their bodies. These animals are known as **vertebrates**.

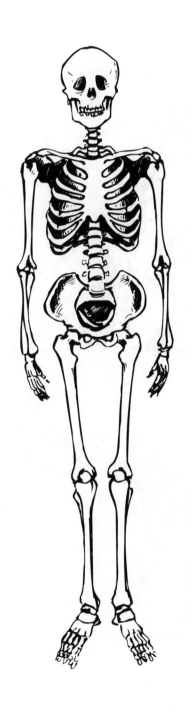

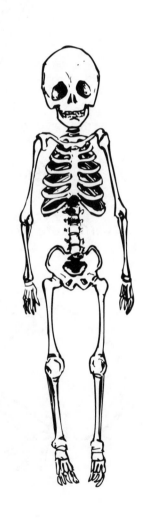

● Label the **ribs**, **spine**, **skull**, **femur**, **pelvis** and **breast bone** on these skeletons.

● Compare the bone in your forearm with that of a friend. Compare it with an adult's arm. What do you notice? What happens to your skeleton as you get older?

Name _____

Vertebrates

- Look at this animal's teeth. (It is a plant eater.)
- Look at the size and position of its eye sockets. (It has very good vision.)
- Look at the long slender legs. (It moves at high speed.)

- What is it? _____

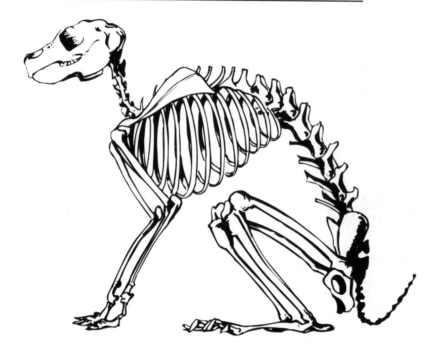

- Identify this vertebrate. Look closely for clues.

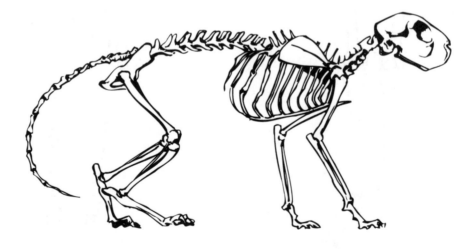

_____

- Compare the skeletons on this sheet with a human skeleton. What is different? What is the same?

_____

_____

_____

Name _____

Animals without bony skeletons

Identify each of these creatures and say how the body is supported.

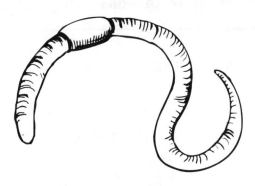

_____

_____

_____

_____

_____

_____

_____

_____

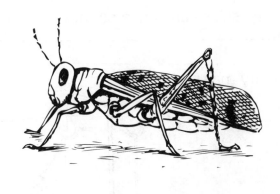

_____

_____

_____

_____

_____

_____

_____

_____

This group of animals is known as **invertebrates**.

PHOTOCOPIABLE

Name _____

Muscles and movement

Muscles are parts of the body that make things move. They are attached to bones by **tendons** – long, flexible cables.

● Feel your muscles when…

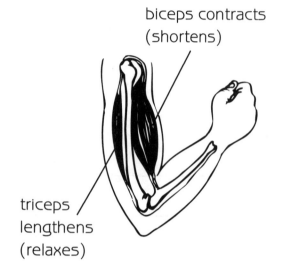

biceps contracts (shortens)

triceps lengthens (relaxes)

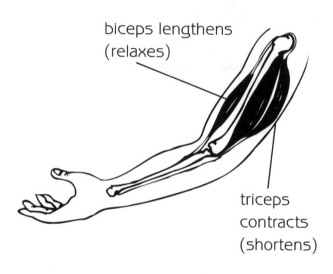

biceps lengthens (relaxes)

triceps contracts (shortens)

… you **bend** your arm.

… **unbend** your arm.

Muscles can't push so they work **in pairs**.

● Try making this.

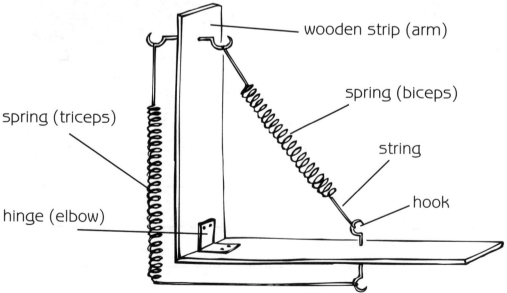

wooden strip (arm)

spring (biceps)

string

hook

spring (triceps)

hinge (elbow)

● The springs are your muscles. What happens to them when the wooden arm is raised and lowered?

NO FUSS
PHOTOCOPIABLE

SCHOLASTIC
www.scholastic.co.uk

Name _____

Organisms

The plants and animals below are all **living things** or **organisms**.
Can you write their names in the correct group?

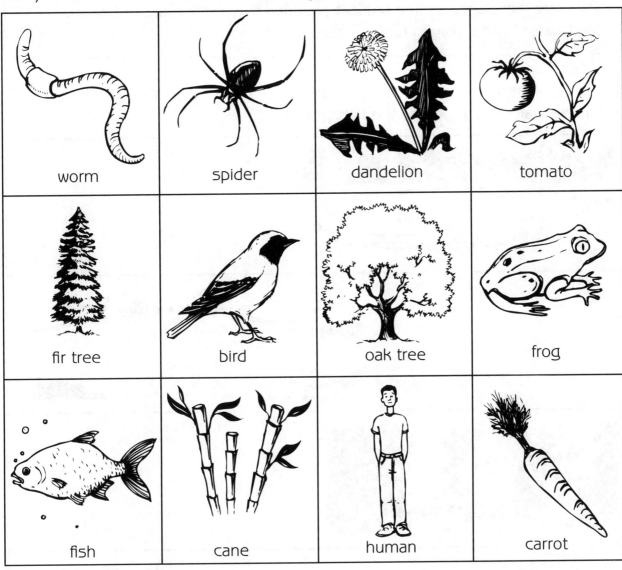

worm	spider	dandelion	tomato
fir tree	bird	oak tree	frog
fish	cane	human	carrot

Plants

_____

_____

_____

_____

_____

_____

Animals

_____

_____

_____

_____

_____

_____

Name _____

Habitats

Plants and animals are found in different types of places called **habitats**. They live there because the **habitat** provides them with sufficient water, food, warmth and oxygen to survive.

● Draw a plant or animal that can be found in each of these habitats. (Draw each one in the blank space next to the habitat.)

● Can you think of another habitat? Draw it on the back of this sheet. Add a plant or animal that might live there.

Identification keys

● Use the key to identify **1**, **2** and **3**.

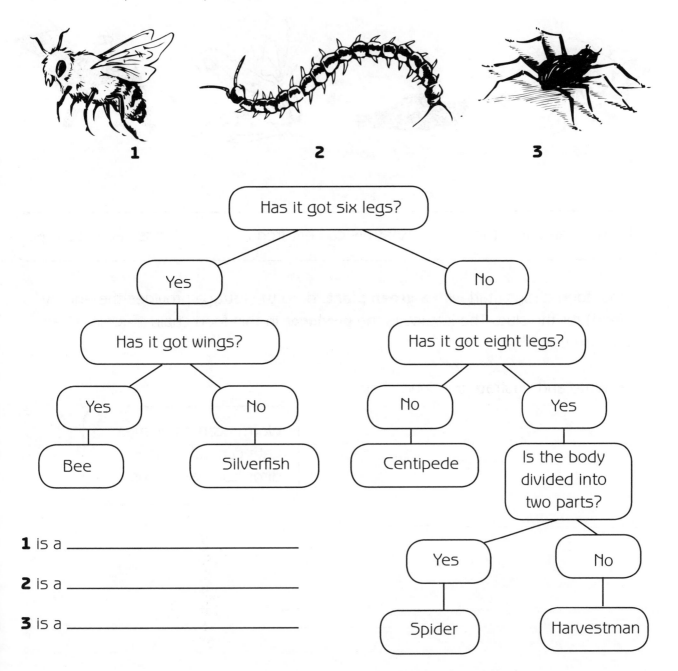

1   **2**   **3**

Has it got six legs?

Yes → Has it got wings?

Yes → Bee

No → Silverfish

No → Has it got eight legs?

No → Centipede

Yes → Is the body divided into two parts?

Yes → Spider

No → Harvestman

1 is a _____

2 is a _____

3 is a _____

● Can you write a key to help your friend identify these two birds?

goose   blackbird

NO
FUSS
PHOTOCOPIABLE

Name _____

Food chains

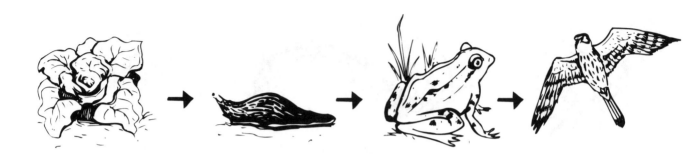

Slugs can eat lettuces.   Kestrels can eat frogs.   Frogs can eat slugs.

Most food chains start with a **green plant**. Here the lettuce provides the energy (food) for the slug. The lettuce is the **producer** in this food chain. Each link eats the one before.

● Write and illustrate this food chain.

Worms can eat leaves.
Cats can eat birds.
Birds can eat worms.

● Name the **producer** in this food chain. _____

Thermometers

● These thermometers have different uses, which is why they look different from each other. Find out what they are called.

● Can you suggest what they might be used for?

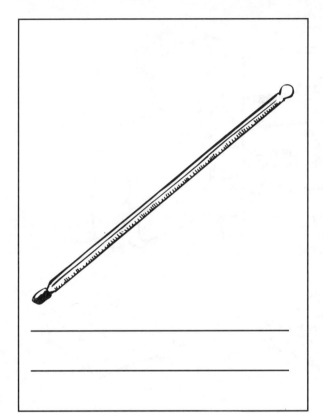

_____

_____

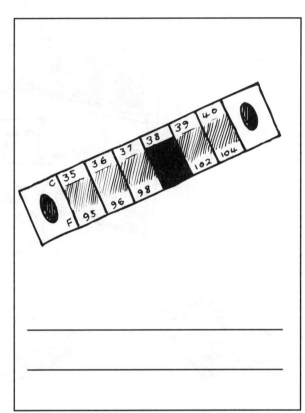

_____

_____

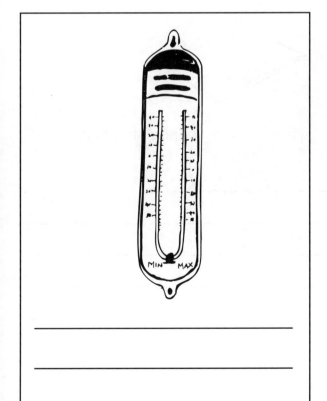

_____

_____

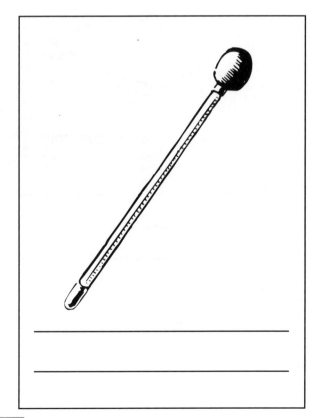

_____

_____

Name _____

Wrap up!

● How could you find out which is the best material for keeping a cold drink cold, once it has been taken out of the fridge? Choose from the pictures below.

newspaper   bubble wrap   polythene

aluminium foil   sponge sheeting

For my test I will need _____

_____

I will _____

_____

_____

● Check: Is your test fair?
● With your teacher's help, carry out your test.

SCHOLASTIC
www.scholastic.co.uk

Name _____

Keeping solids and liquids apart

● Are these **solids** or **liquids**? Put **L** or **S** in the boxes.

car oil ☐	sponge ☐	milk ☐	chocolate ☐	cola ☐
tea ☐	chair ☐	jelly ☐	rice ☐	ice cream ☐
shampoo ☐	cotton wool ☐	hairspray ☐	cooking oil ☐	salt ☐

● How are solids and liquids different from each other? What shape are they? Can you pour them? Can you spill them? Write some of your ideas in this table.

properties of solids	properties of liquids

PHOTOCOPIABLE

Name _____

Separate (1)

● Make a mixture from these:

sand   rice   paper clips   dried peas

● Can you separate them?
Here are some ideas of what you might need:

colander   sieve

● Can you think of other ways to separate the materials?
Write down what you could do.

_____

_____

_____

_____

_____

_____

_____

Name _____

What happens when?

● Draw what happens when you mix water with these materials.

 **+**  **=**

 **+**  **=**

 **+**  **=**

 **+**  **=**

● Can you explain what happens?
● Repeat with powder paint, chalk, sand, marbles and plaster of Paris.
● Record your results in a table.

Name _____

Separate (2)

● Make a mixture of sand and water.
● Try to separate the sand from the water by **filtering**. Make filters from these things.

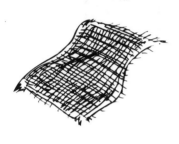

muslin

paper towels

gauze bandage   blotting paper

tea bags

coffee filters

fabrics

● Explain what happened in your experiment.

_____

_____

_____

_____

_____

_____

● Can you separate a solution of salt and water or sugar and water in the same way?

_____

_____

SCHOLASTIC
www.scholastic.co.uk

Friction

Friction is the force between two things rubbing together.
Friction usually makes things hot. Rub your hands together!

Complete the table with some ideas of your own.

High friction	Low friction
car tyres	skating
bicyle tyres	sliding
goalkeeper's gloves	
tying shoelaces	

Name _____

Friction and force meters

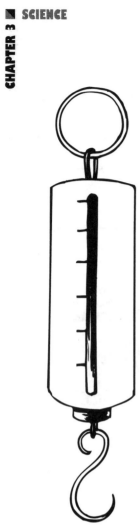

● Read the force meter...

...when your friend pulls on it ☐ newtons

...when you pull open a drawer ☐ newtons

...when you drag an object across the floor. ☐ newtons

● On what kind of surface do objects slide more easily?

_____

● Test three different surfaces, for example wood, vinyl, carpet. Choose two more surfaces. Carry out a fair test and record your results on this bar chart.

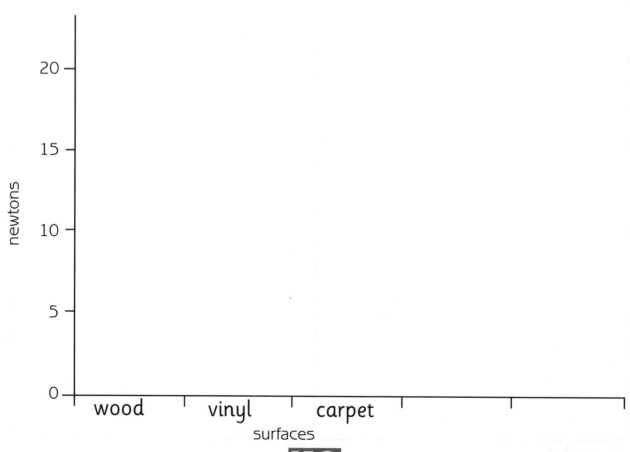

NO FUSS
PHOTOCOPIABLE

Name _____

Good conductors

Materials that electricity will flow through are called **conductors**.
Materials that electricity cannot flow through are called **insulators**.

● Use a circuit like this to see which materials are best for conducting electricity.
Try bridging the gap with these materials.

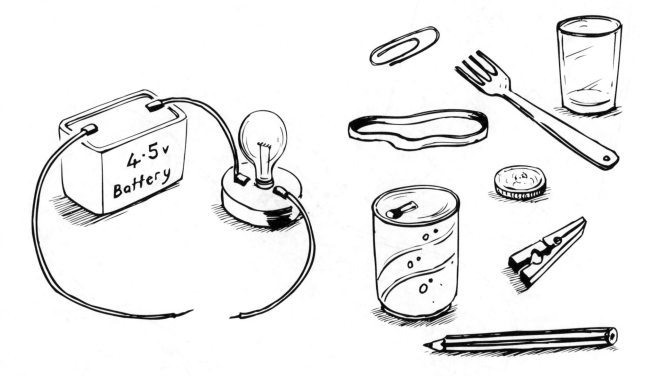

● Which materials make the bulb light up?
● What else can you test? Fill in this chart.

conductors	insulators

Name _____

Making and breaking

A **circuit** must be complete for a device to work.

● Which **two corners** must be touched with the wires to complete this circuit and make the bulb light? _____

● Make a puzzle like this for a friend to try.

● A **switch** is a device for breaking a circuit. Why do we need switches?

_____

_____

_____

_____

Who was Henry VIII?

Henry VIII became king of England nearly 500 years ago. He ruled from 1509 to 1547. He was the eighth king with the name Henry so he was known as Henry the eighth. (In Roman numerals V=5 III=3, so VIII=8.) He belonged to the Tudor family and the Tudor rose, which was both red and white, was its symbol.

King Henry VIII by Hans the Younger Holbein (1497/8–1543), Thyssen-Bornemisza Collection, Madrid, Spain/Bridgeman Art Library

● Study his portrait carefully. What does the picture tell you about Henry? Finish the sentences below.

I think that Henry was

_____

_____

_____

I think this because

_____

_____

_____

I also think that Henry was

_____

_____

_____

I think this because

_____

_____

_____

● Use reference books to help you colour in the rose.

Name _____

Henry's queens

Henry VIII had six wives. This rhyme tells what happened to them – in order.

> Divorced, beheaded, died.
> Divorced, beheaded, survived.

● Cut out the portraits of the queens and stick them in the correct places.

divorced (1533)	beheaded (1536)	died (1537)

divorced (1540)	beheaded (1542)	survived Henry VIII

Anne of Cleves. Married in 1540. Only married for a few months.

Catherine Howard. Married in 1540.

Jane Seymour. Married in 1536. Died after her son Edward was born.

Catherine of Aragon. Married in 1509. Had a daughter Mary.

Catherine Parr. Married in 1543. Clever and well-educated, she outlived the King.

Anne Boleyn. Married in 1533. Had a daughter Elizabeth.

NO FUSS PHOTOCOPIABLE

■ SCHOLASTIC
www.scholastic.co.uk

Name _____

Henry VIII: did and didn't

● What did King Henry VIII actually do? Sort these sentences into two groups,
Did and **Didn't**.

He met ambassadors from other countries.
He talked with advisors about money and other business.
He did housework.
He led the army into battle.
He went hunting.
He did gardening.
He wrote and played music.
He went to church regularly.
He played sport.
He attended grand banquets.
He signed government papers and laws.
He bought and sold things.

Name _____

A comfortable house

The houses of poor people who lived in Tudor times were so badly built that they did not last long. Most of the Tudor houses that survive today were built by people who were comfortably off – farmers, merchants and professional people such as lawyers.

● Fit these labels correctly.

oak framework

brick in-fill between timbers

brick chimney

window bars (no glass panes – shutters were used at night)

wattle and daub in-fill (woven hazel twigs plastered over with a mixture of dung, clay, lime and straw)

● Find out more about Tudor houses.
● Write an estate agent's description of this house as if you were trying to sell it.

A list of clues

> We can learn a great deal about what it was like in Tudor times from documents that have survived. Inventories (lists of house contents) and wills tell us what people owned and valued.

This is part of Isabel Watkinson's will (1492). Read it carefully. What do you notice about the spelling? Make a list of the things she gave away. Who did she give them to?

In the name of God, amen.

I Isabell Watkinson, of good health and perfecte remembrance but sycke in body, do make this laste will and testamente.

I bequeathe my soule to almighty God my maker and to Jesus Christ his Son my Savioure and Redeemer and my bodye to be buried in the paryshe churche of Heath.

Item: I give and bequeathe to my son Rycharde all my corn in the folde and all my croppe of corne in my barne savinge that he shall give to Humphrey my son half a quarter of harderaine.

Item: I give also to my son Rycharde my beste potte and my best panne.

Item: I give and bequeathe unto Humphrey my said sone my beste potte and my beste panne next and all the rest of my brasse to be equally divided amongste all my children generallye, both sonse and daughters.

Item: I give and bequeathe to Rycharde my said sone three of my beste dublers.

Item: I give and bequeathe to Rycharde my said sone two of my beste cattell, the cattell remaynest to my other children, everyone of them.

Item: I give and bequeathe to Mary Bakon a ringed heffer about two years olde.

Item: I give and bequeathe to Rycharde my said sone one ffether bedde and a boulster and the coverlytt which ye yet arranged to make – a new coverlytt.

Item: I gyve to my sons Robert Watkinson's children everyone of them, 12 pence.

Item: I give and bequeathe unto my three daughters, Jane, Agnes and Alice, all my apparyll and all my apparyll wayre in my cheste which dost stand by my bedde heade.

Item: I wyll that Robert Watkinson's childe to my sone Robert Watkinson shall have the counter table in the house and a share in two great chests in the boultinge house.

Item: I give and bequeathe unto Humphrey my said sone two shepe. And all the rest of the shepe I give to Rycharde my sone.

Item: I give and bequeathe to William Harryson my servante two yards of empon cloth to make him a shirt.

I the sayd Isabell Watkinson have to this laste wyll and testamente sett my hand and marke.

Name _____

The Second World War

This map shows some of the events of the Second World War. Why was it called a 'world' war? Choose one of the places shown on the map and write a paragraph about what happened there. You will have to do some research like a historian!

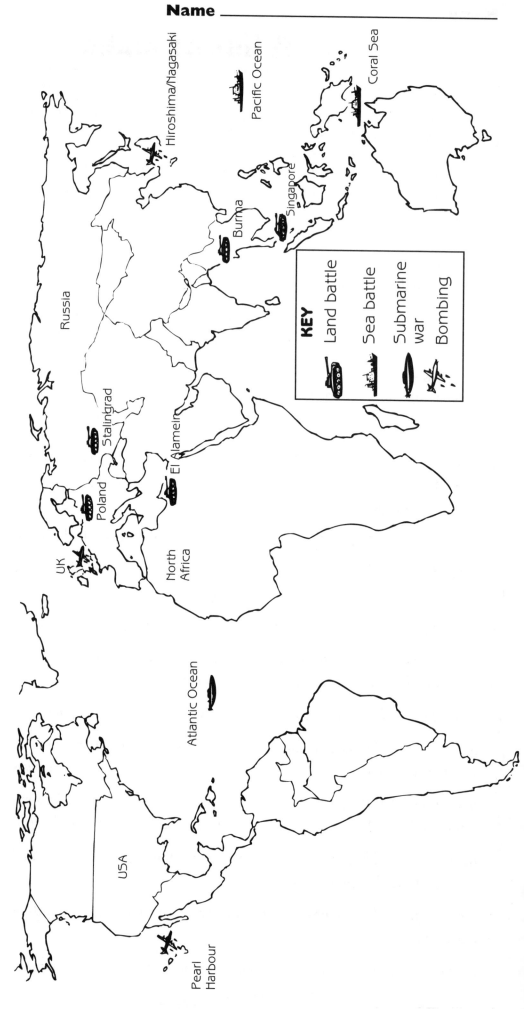

Hiroshima/Nagasaki

Coral Sea

Pacific Ocean

Singapore

Burma

Russia

KEY
Land battle
Sea battle
Submarine war
Bombing

Stalingrad

El Alamein

Poland

North Africa

UK

Atlantic Ocean

USA

Pearl Harbour

NO FUSS
PHOTOCOPIABLE

■SCHOLASTIC
www.scholastic.co.uk

World War II timeline

Cut out these strips. Arrange them in the correct time order. Stick them on a large sheet of paper and illustrate the timeline. Add more detailed information.

✂

1942	The British defeat the German and Italian armies at El Alamein.
1944	The Allies land an army in Normandy in order to recapture Europe from the Germans.
1939	The first evacuation of children from cities begins in Britain.
1941	Without warning the Japanese bomb the Americans at Pearl Harbour.
1940	Winston Churchill becomes Prime Minister.
1945	Germany surrenders.
1943	The Russians defeat the Germans in the battle for the city of Stalingrad.
1945	USA drops atomic bombs on the Japanese cities of Hiroshima and Nagasaki. Japan surrenders. The Second World War ends.
1940	German air force begins heavy bombing of London and other British cities.

Name _____

Evacuation

● Look carefully at this poster. What is it trying to persuade people to do? Why?

● What was the Ministry of Health Evacuation Scheme? Who was it for? Why only them?

Public Record Office Image Library

● Design a poster of your own to try to get people to join the scheme.

Name _____

Ancient Egypt: model behaviour

- These wooden carvings were found in caves on the bank of the river Nile in Egypt. Look carefully. What do they tell us about life in Ancient Egypt?

- Can you find and label: a woman kneading dough to make bread, a brewer soaking barley for beer making, a water carrier lifting jars of water, a man pounding grain to make flour?

Model of servants making bread and brewing, Egyptian, early XII Dynasty, 1963–1862BC (painted wood, linen and clay). Fitzwilliam Museum, University of Cambridge, UK/Bridgeman Art Library.

Name _____

Land of the Nile

The Ancient Egyptians needed the river Nile. It flooded to give them fertile soil on which to grow crops.

The Nile delta (where the river spread out to meet the sea in the north) was fertile land. This was called Lower Egypt. The narrow valley of the river was called Upper Egypt.

Egypt is surrounded by desert (known as the Red Land) where Egyptians hunted and found stone for building. The pyramids were built on the edge of the desert because fertile soil (the Black Land) was too precious for building on.

The Nile is 4187 miles long, the longest river in the world. About 60 million people live in Egypt today, in ancient times it was probably only 3 million.

Colour and label this map using the facts you have learned.

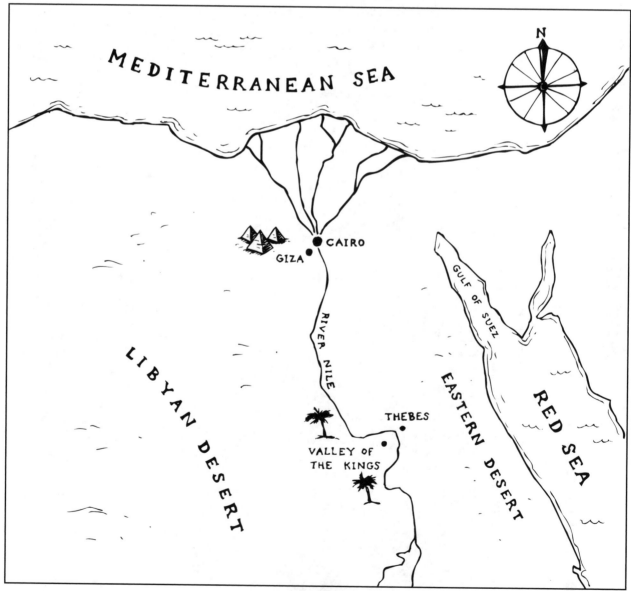

SCHOLASTIC
www.scholastic.co.uk

Name _____

What a load of rubbish!

Estimate, then weigh, your classroom rubbish each day and record your results.

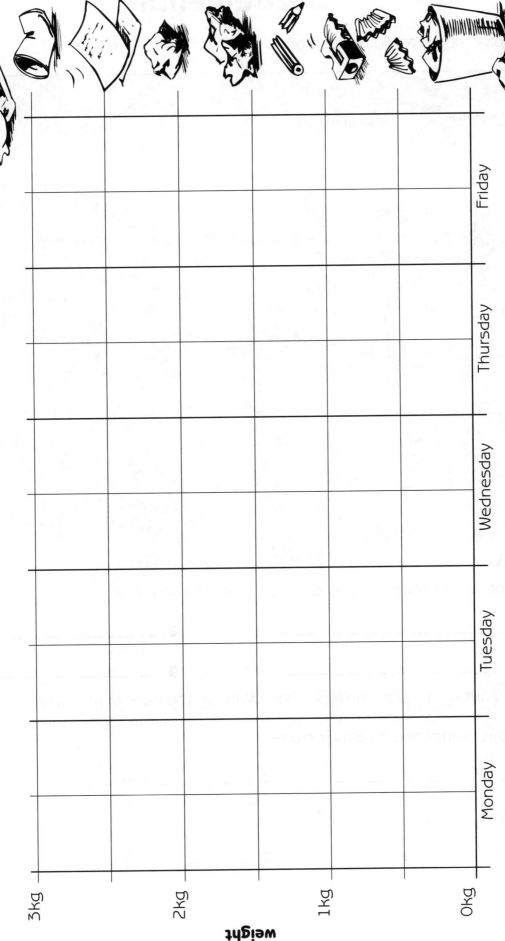

weight

3kg

2kg

1kg

0kg

Monday

Tuesday

Wednesday

Thursday

Friday

days of the week

NO FUSS
PHOTOCOPIABLE

Name _____

Settlements

● Look carefully at this section of an OS (Ordnance Survey®) map.

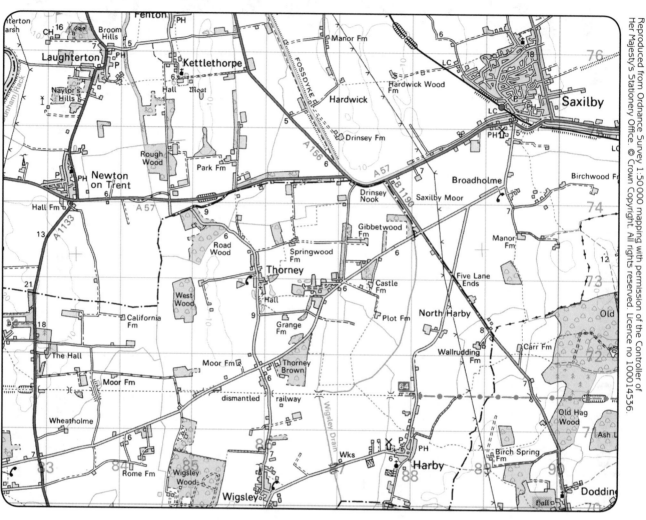

● Choose four villages/towns ending in -by, -ton and -thorpe.

1. _____   2. _____

3. _____   4. _____

● Find out what these endings mean. Write on the back of the sheet.

● Is the village/town on a river crossing?

1. _____   2. _____   3. _____   4. _____

● Is there flat land for farming?

1. _____   2. _____   3. _____   4. _____

● Is there any danger of flooding?

1. _____   2. _____   3. _____   4. _____

Name _____

Where am I?

● On this map, Little Newbury is in square 3092. Find it.

30 (the number along the bottom)
92 (the number up the side)

Remember we go in the door

before going up the stairs.

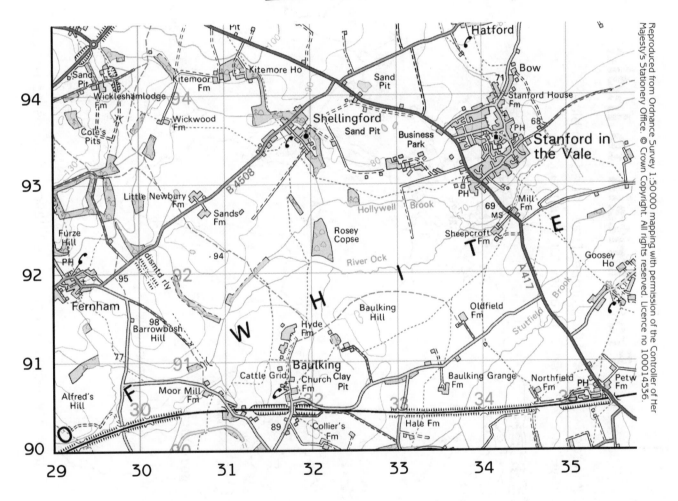

● What can you find in these squares on the map?

3493 _____

3292 _____

3093 _____

2990 _____

Name _____

From Britain to India

- ● Find Britain. Draw round it in red.
- ● Find Asia. Draw round it in yellow.
- ● Find Europe. Draw round it in blue.
- ● Draw a key for your map.
- ● Find India. Draw round it in green.

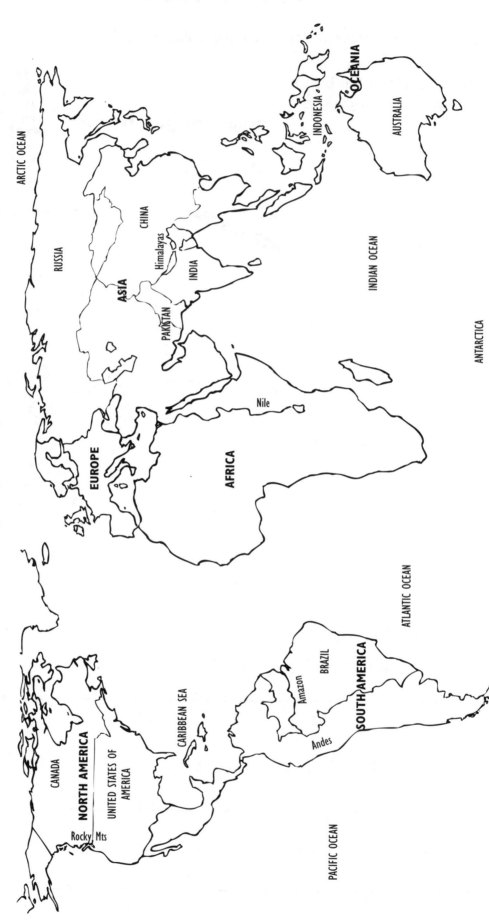

ARCTIC OCEAN

RUSSIA

CHINA

ASIA

Himalayas

INDIA

PAKISTAN

INDONESIA

OCEANIA

AUSTRALIA

INDIAN OCEAN

ANTARCTICA

EUROPE

Nile

AFRICA

CANADA

NORTH AMERICA

UNITED STATES OF AMERICA

Rocky Mts

CARIBBEAN SEA

Amazon

BRAZIL

SOUTH AMERICA

Andes

ATLANTIC OCEAN

PACIFIC OCEAN

- ● Plan a route to India from Britain. How would you get there? Which countries would you cross? Which airports would you use?

NO FUSS
PHOTOCOPIABLE

Name _____

An Indian market

© TRIP/H Rogers

- How can you tell it is hot?
- Why do people wear loose-fitting clothes?
- Find out about saris, dhotis and lungis.
- Compare this market with your local market.

- Identify these foods found in an Indian market. Would we eat them raw or cooked?

orange

cauliflower

aubergine

chilli

guava

coriander

ginger

Name _____

How do you spend your time?

Fill in each category with as much information as you can.

work

reading

piano playing

football

recreation

leisure

Name _____

How do you spend your time: a questionnaire

This questionnaire is not finished. Complete the questions and then hand a copy to each child in the class to fill in the data.

	What?	**Where?**			**How long?** (per week)		
		home	school	other	2 hours or more	1 hour	½ hour or less
WORK	housework ____ ____ ____ ____	☐☐☐☐☐	☐☐☐☐☐	☐☐☐☐☐	☐☐☐☐☐	☐☐☐☐☐	☐☐☐☐☐
LEISURE	reading ____ ____ ____ ____	☐☐☐☐☐	☐☐☐☐☐	☐☐☐☐☐	☐☐☐☐☐	☐☐☐☐☐	☐☐☐☐☐
RECREATION	skating ____ ____ ____ ____	☐☐☐☐☐	☐☐☐☐☐	☐☐☐☐☐	☐☐☐☐☐	☐☐☐☐☐	☐☐☐☐☐

NO FUSS PHOTOCOPIABLE

Money in materials

● Look at these money containers. What materials do you think they are made from? Why?

● Label the following on the drawings above:

| seam | strap | hem | press stud |

| zip | Velcro | buckle | button |

● How do they fasten? Can you think of any other fasteners?

● Design and make a purse or wallet.
  • Who will use it?
  • What material will it be made from?
  • How will it fasten?

NO FUSS
PHOTOCOPIABLE

■SCHOLASTIC
www.scholastic.co.uk

Sew a seam

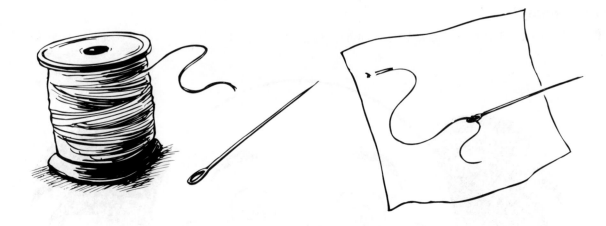

● Start and finish on the wrong side of the material by making a few stitches on top of each other. Practise these stitches:

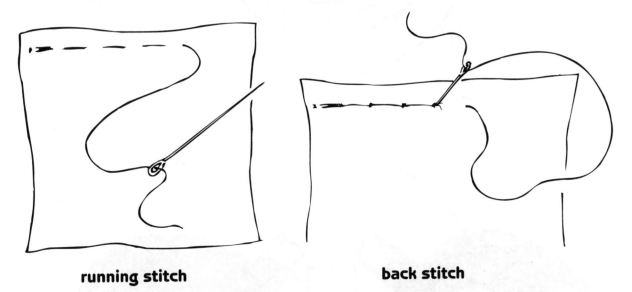

running stitch

back stitch

● Which is the strongest joining stitch? Investigate:

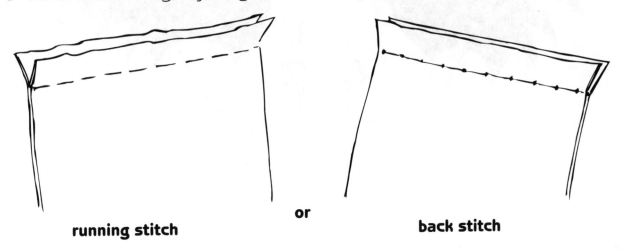

running stitch

or

back stitch

● In what other ways can we join two pieces of material together? Investigate.

Name _____

Controlling comic clown (1)

Hair-raising!

● Explain to a friend how the clown's hair is raised.

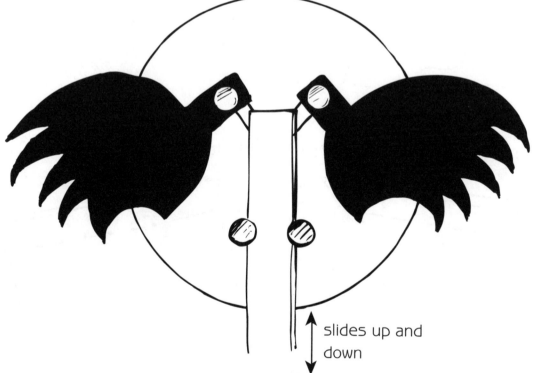

slides up and down

● Now it's your turn. Make the clown's head from stiff card and use card strips and paper fasteners to make his eyes, nose or ears move.

NO FUSS
PHOTOCOPIABLE

■ **SCHOLASTIC**
www.scholastic.co.uk

Controlling comic clown (2)

Are you switched on? (1)

- Can you see how these two **pressure switches** work?
- Can you make a similar **pressure switch** but use foil?

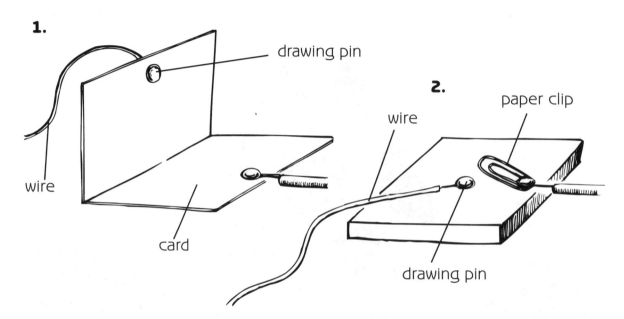

1.

drawing pin

wire

card

2.

paper clip

wire

drawing pin

- How do you think this **trip switch** works?

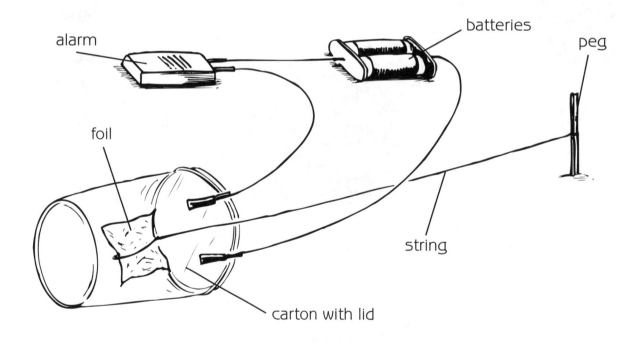

alarm

batteries

peg

foil

string

carton with lid

_____

_____

_____

_____

NO FUSS PHOTOCOPIABLE

Name _____

Are you switched on? (2)

How do you think this **rain switch** works?

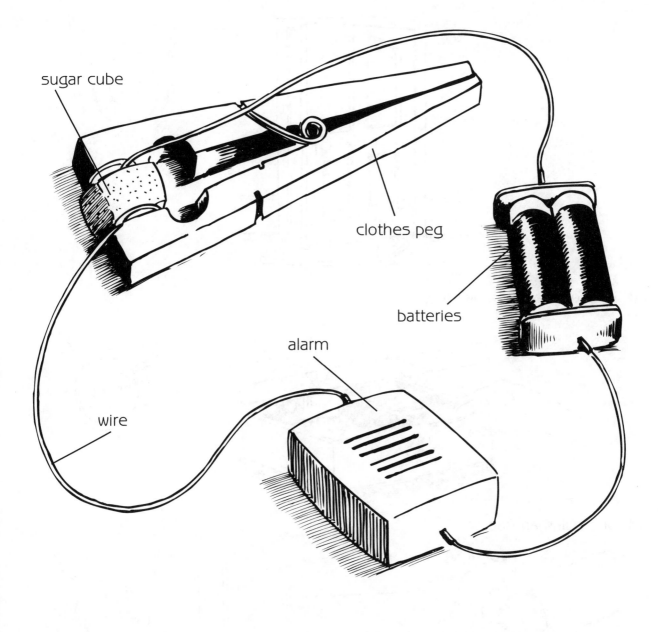

sugar cube

clothes peg

batteries

alarm

wire

_____

_____

_____

_____

_____

_____

Name _____

Alarming!

● Design and make an alarm for a door being opened

● or a jewellery box being opened

● or a milkman trap.

Things you might need:	wire	drawing pins	battery
alarm	pegs	foil	paper clips	card

Name _____

A place for colour

Scan this black and white design into your computer (ask your teacher). Colour the shapes to make an exciting design. Save your work, then print it out.

(scan)   (save as)   (copy)   (print)

Name _____

Yes or no?

● This is a _____ .

● Put a tick by all the questions below that can be answered **yes** or **no**.
● If someone could not see the object above, which **yes** or **no** questions would help them to work out what it was? Cut them out and then arrange them in the best order.

How many legs has it got? ☐

Is it made of metal? ☐

How big is it? ☐

Can you pick it up? ☐

Is it used in the house? ☐

What is it made of? ☐

Is it used in the garage? ☐

What room in the house is it used in? ☐

Has it got a handle? ☐

What do we use it for? ☐

Is it used for cooking? ☐

Do we watch it? ☐

Can I turn it on? ☐

Is it big or small? ☐

Do we boil eggs in it? ☐

Do we have one in the classroom? ☐

What colour is it? ☐

What does it taste like? ☐

Can I eat it? ☐

Name _____

Graphs for a purpose

● These charts and graphs show different data. Give each one a title.

Sunday

Monday

1. _____

_____

2. _____

_____

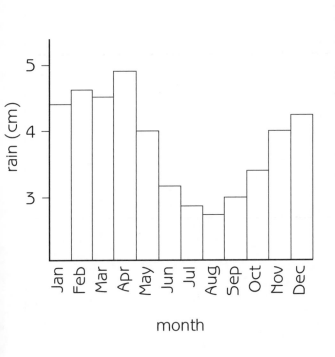

3. _____

_____

4. _____

_____

● Collect data on the number of boys and girls in your **class**. Use ICT to make a pie chart of your data.

● Collect data on the number of boys and girls in your **school**. Use ICT to make a pie chart. What can you learn by comparing the two charts you have made?

Turning turtle

Use the screen turtle (LOGO) to test the following instructions. Sketch what you think will appear on the screen.

Commands	My prediction
forward 80, right 90, forward 80, left 90, forward 80, right 90, forward 80, left 90, forward 80, right 90, forward 80, left 90, forward 80	
forward 150, right 90, forward 150, right 90, forward 150, right 90, forward 150	
forward 180, right 120, forward 180, right 120, forward 180, right 120	
forward 120, right 90 (repeat four times)	
forward 100, left 6 (repeat six times)	

Varying viewpoints

● Use your viewfinder in the school grounds to find unusual and different viewpoints.

down

around

up

through

reflection

underneath

● Sketch each view in your sketchbook.

Name _____

Collograph

● Use a photo or video image, or a sketch from your sketchbook, to develop your own personal design.

You will need (for the printing block):

strong card
matchsticks
PVA glue
wool
string
textured fabric

You will also need:

printing ink   paint roller   large sheet of plain paper   old magazines

Instructions

● Make your printing block. Form shapes out of different materials and place them onto card. Link and overlap them. Make them touch the edge of the card.

● Now glue the shapes onto your piece of card securely and wait for them to dry.

● Cover the shapes on the card with water-based printing ink using a roller.

● Using the block, print one colour several times onto the large sheet of paper, rubbing into corners with fingertips.

● Remove traces of ink from the card using old magazines.

● Change colour and print a shadow image, slightly to one side of the first image, to create a pleasing design.

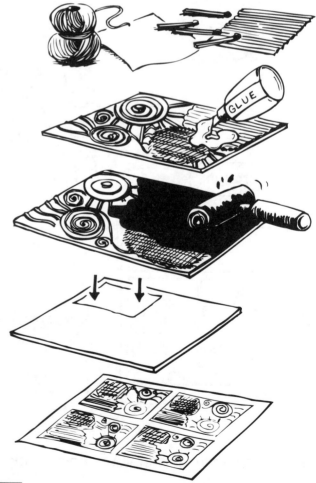

NO FUSS
PHOTOCOPIABLE

■**SCHOLASTIC**
www.scholastic.co.uk

Dream art

Study this photograph carefully. It takes you into a dream world. Make a print design called 'Dreams' using ideas suggested by this photograph.

Name _____

Choose a chair

● Study these chairs.

● Look at the shape and height of the seats and their backrests.
● How are the chairs similar? How are the chairs different?
● How are the chairs used? What is their purpose?
● What are they made of?
● How are they made?

● Design a chair for an unusual character.
● Construct a scale model chair, using cards, tubes or other suitable materials.

■SCHOLASTIC
www.scholastic.co.uk

Take five: the pentatonic scale

● Use the five chime bars to practise these **ostinati**.

1	2	3	1	2	3	1	2	3	
	●			●	●		●		repeat...
●		●	●			●		●	
C	E	D	C	E	D	C	E	D	

				●		●		●	
●			●			●			repeat...
	●				●		●		
G	E	A	G	E	A	G	E	A	

1	2	3	4	1	2	3	4	1	2	3	4	
			●			●				●	●	repeat...
		●			●				●			
●	●			●				●				
C	D	E	G	C	D	E	G	C	D	E	G	

●				●				●				
	●				●				●			repeat...
		●				●				●		
			●				●				●	
G	E	D	C	G	E	D	C	G	E	D	C	

● Play them with a friend. Play two different ostinati at the same time. Which go together best?

● Write an ostinato using *only* these five notes: C, D, E, G, A.

NO FUSS
PHOTOCOPIABLE

Name _____

Take five into the forest

Pentatonic tunes are composed using a special five-note scale. Pentatonic tunes have been sung for hundreds of years in many countries over the world. You may think that they sound oriental. A lot of music uses this scale. Here is a pentatonic scale.

● Play this tune using the pentatonic scale.

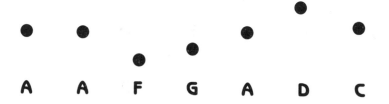

A   A   F   G   A   D   C

● Compose your own tune (use seven notes). Start anywhere! Repeat notes! Write it down here.

● Use the pentatonic scale to accompany this short story. Add drums and percussion with a friend.

The boy entered the dark, dark forest.
The leaves rustled in a gentle breeze.
Suddenly two dogs came crashing through the bushes.
A flock of birds flew up and a cuckoo sang.
The boy turned and ran out of the forest, leaping over stones and clumps of grass.

Mood music

● Music can create different moods and different pictures in the mind. What is your favourite tune? _____

● How does it make you feel? _____

_____

_____

● Look at this picture. Write down as many words and phrases as you can that fit the mood of this picture.

● Use instruments to create sounds that match your words and this picture.

Name _____

Sounds and pictures

● Work with a friend. What is happening here? Write down words that describe the picture. List words and phrases that describe how it makes you feel.

● Choose instruments and paint this picture in sound.

© Corel

PHOTOCOPIABLE

■SCHOLASTIC
www.scholastic.co.uk

Game for a song (1)

● With some friends, learn this game.

One, two
Buckle my shoe;
Three, four
Knock at the door;
Five, six
Pick up sticks;
Seven, eight
Lay them straight;
Nine, ten
A big fat hen.

● What kind of game is it? Put a circle round the words that fit.

choosing   clapping   skipping

ball game   dancing   counting

● Play an untuned percussion instrument while the game is being played. Can you play the pulse?

Name _____

Game for a song (2)

● This is an American singing game. Read the words. Put a circle round the sort of game you think it might be.

I've been to Har-lem, I've been to Do-ver, I've tra-velled this wide world all o-ver.

O-ver, o-ver, three times o-ver, Drink what you have to drink and turn the glass-es o-ver.

Sail-ing east, sail-ing west, Sail-ing o-ver the o- cean,

Bet-ter watch out when the boat be-gins to rock, or you'll lose your girl in the o- cean.

choosing	clapping	skipping
ball game	dancing	counting

● Explain your choices.

● Sing the song and play a game that fits it.

SCHOLASTIC
www.scholastic.co.uk

Aum

The Hindu symbol for God is **aum**. This is what it looks like:

It is pronounced 'om' and sometimes written that way. The symbol is sacred and so is the sound 'om'. The symbol appears in Hindu homes and places of worship. The sound is used to start and end Hindu prayers.

● Copy the **aum** symbol here.

● Hindus believe there is one God but that there are different images of him. Find out about Ganesh and Krishna.

Name _____

Where is God? A Hindu story

This story illustrates a Hindu belief about God.
Cut out the pictures and arrange them in the correct order for the story
to make sense.

How far is it to Bethlehem?

● Find Bethlehem on this map. Then find Bethlehem in an atlas. Work out how far away it is from where you live.

● Why is Bethlehem important to Christians?

_____

_____

● Tell the story of a journey to Bethlehem by one of the following:

(Mary and Joseph)   (the wise men)   (the shepherds)

Name _____

A Christmas carol

Christians sing songs about the birth of Jesus. These are called **carols**.

Words © Stainer and Bell

Here we go up to Beth - le - hem, Beth - le - hem, Beth - le - hem.

Here we go up to Beth - le - hem on a cold and frost - ty morn — ing.

We've got to be taxed in Bethlehem,
Bethlehem, Bethlehem,
We've got to be taxed in Bethlehem
On a cold and frosty morning.

Sydney Carter

● Write a verse of your own to this tune (it's from 'Here we go round the Mulberry Bush'), telling another part of the Christmas story.

NO FUSS
PHOTOCOPIABLE

The Easter story (1): Palm Sunday

● Find out when **Palm Sunday** is (look in a diary).

● Why do Christians call it Palm Sunday?

● Read the story here and then compare with the one in the Bible (Matthew 21:1–11).

● Churches often give out **palm crosses** on Palm Sunday. Can you make one?

1. Jesus and his disciples approached the city of Jerusalem. At Bethany, Jesus sent two of his disciples ahead to fetch a donkey.

2. They brought the donkey and laid their cloaks on its back for Jesus to ride.

3. Along the route crowds gathered. They laid cloaks and palm branches in front of the donkey.

4. When Jesus entered Jerusalem, the crowd went wild with excitement. "Who is this?" some people asked. "It is the prophet Jesus from Nazareth," shouted the crowd.

RELIGIOUS EDUCATION

Name _____

The Easter story (2): the Last Supper

● This is a painting of the last meal Jesus ate with his disciples. You can read the story for yourself (Mark 14:12–26). Describe what is happening in this picture.

The Last Supper (oil on panel) by German School (16th century), Wilanow Palace, Warsaw, Poland/Bridgeman Art Library

● Because they ate bread and drank wine with Jesus, Christians do the same today in the **Eucharist**. Find out all you can about the Eucharist.

NO FUSS PHOTOCOPIABLE

■SCHOLASTIC www.scholastic.co.uk

The Easter story (3)

This cartoon tells the Easter story. First cut out the pictures and arrange them in the correct order. Then cut out and match the correct words to the pictures.

Judas betrays Jesus with a kiss in the Garden of Gethsemane.	Jesus is crucified with the two bandits at Golgotha.
The High Priest asks Jesus whether he is the Messiah. "I am," he replies.	Jesus is placed in a rock tomb sealed by a huge stone.
Pilate, the Roman governor, can find no harm in Jesus. To satisfy the crowd, he condemns Jesus to be crucified.	On the third day his followers find the tomb empty. They are afraid.

Name _____

Rules and laws protect us (1)

● What laws or rules are being broken in the pictures?
● Explain how the law or rule protects everyone.

Law being broken

_____

_____

How this law protects us

_____

_____

_____

_____

Law being broken

_____

_____

How this law protects us

_____

_____

_____

_____

Law being broken

_____

_____

How this law protects us

_____

_____

_____

_____

Rules and laws protect us (2)

- Which school rules are being broken in these pictures?
- Explain how the rule protects everyone.

Rule being broken

_____
_____

How this rule protects us

_____
_____
_____
_____
_____

Rule being broken

_____
_____

How this rule protects us

_____
_____
_____
_____
_____

Rule being broken

_____
_____

How this rule protects us

_____
_____
_____
_____

Community connections

● Do you know the names of all the communities that you belong to?
Write their names in the right links.

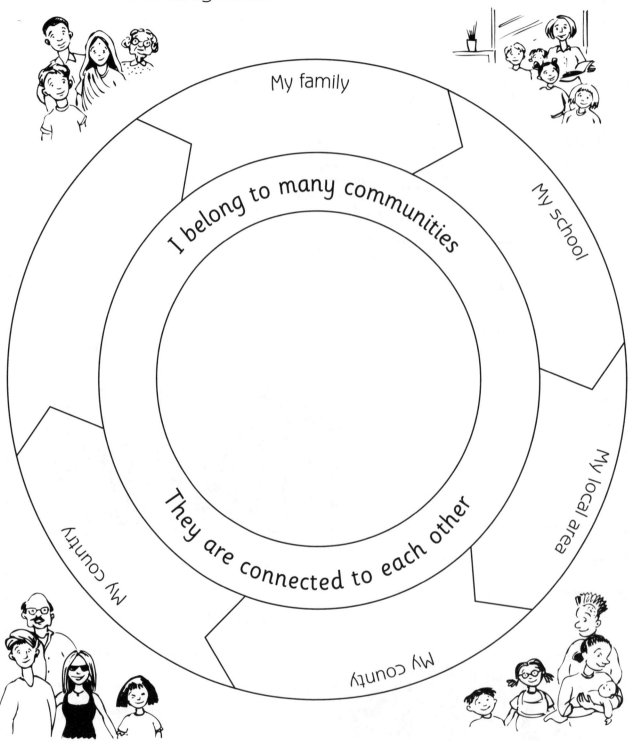

● Can you think of another community that you
belong to? Write it in the blank link.

Heroes and heroines

● Who are your heroes or heroines? Draw their portraits in these frames.
● Why do you admire them? What don't you admire about them?

I admire _____

_____

_____

I don't admire _____

_____

_____

I admire _____

_____

_____

I don't admire _____

_____

_____

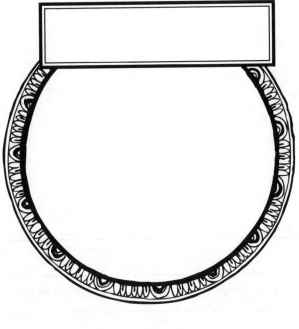

I admire _____

_____

_____

I don't admire _____

_____

_____

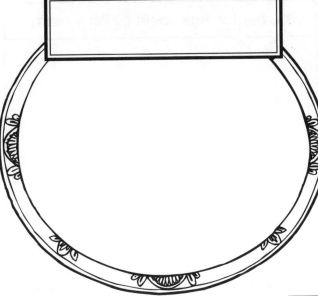

Name _____

In other people's shoes

The good things about being a dad	The hard things about being a dad

The good things about being a mum	The hard things about being a mum

NO FUSS
PHOTOCOPIABLE

■SCHOLASTIC
www.scholastic.co.uk

Name _____

What we do for each other

What I do to help

at home _____

_____

_____

_____

at school _____

_____

_____

_____

_____

What _____ at home does for me

_____

_____

_____

_____

■SCHOLASTIC

In this series:

ISBN 978-1407-10093-7

ISBN 978-1407-10094-4

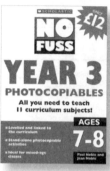

ISBN 978-1407-10095-1

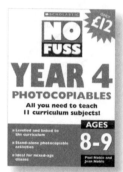

ISBN 978-1407-10096-8

ISBN 978-1407-10097-5

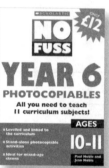

ISBN 978-1407-10098-2

ISBN 978-0439-96548-4

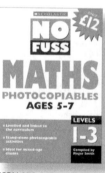

ISBN 978-0439-96550-7

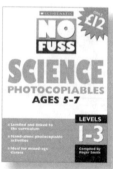

ISBN 978-0439-96552-1

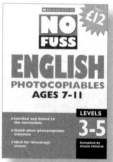

ISBN 978-0439-96549-1

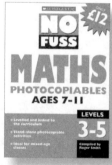

ISBN 978-0439-96551-4

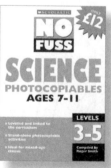

ISBN 978-0439-96553-8

To find out more, call: 0845 603 9091
or visit our website www.scholastic.co.uk